LESBIANS TALK (SAFER) SEX

LESBIANS TALK

Sue O'Sullivan
and Pratibha Parmar

Scarlet Press

Published by Scarlet Press
5 Montague Road, London E8 2HN

British Library Cataloguing-in-Publication Data
A catalogue record for this book is available from the British Library
ISBN 1 85727 020 7

In the same series:
LESBIANS TALK QUEER NOTIONS *Cherry Smyth*

Series editors: Belinda Budge and Vicky Wilson
Cover design: Pat Kahn
Typesetting: Kathryn Holliday
Printed in Great Britain

Contents

Acknowledgments

We would like to thank Beth Zemsky for her stimulating chapter on lesbians and safer sex, written specially for this book, and Da Choong and Teresa Edmans for agreeing to be interviewed at length. The thoughts and knowledge of all three women helped us tremendously. We would also like to thank Nasreen Memon and Madhu for their responses and Nasreen Memon for compiling the list of information and contacts and the bibliography. Thanks also to Belinda Budge and Vicky Wilson from Scarlet Press for their encouragement, support and skilful editing.

Sue I would like to thank Sarah Schulman and Cindy Patton from the US for their separate, lively engagements with me about lesbian safer sex and for their friendship. I would also like to thank British friends, Kate Thomson and Sheila Gilchrist, who have always been willing to explore contradictions around AIDS and sexuality and at the same time remain feisty and funny. Araba Mercer, Michelle McKenzie, Frankie Lynch, Robin Gorna and Sue Katz have all been keen participants in endless wild and exciting discussions on sex and politics. Several gay friends and colleagues have helped me out with information, ideas, arguments. Thanks to Simon Watney, Stuart Marshall and Edward King in Britain. I am always impressed by their continuing commitment to fighting AIDS. Finally and again, for love, support, talk, fun and games, and meals together, thanks to my amazing lover, Mitch Cleary.

Pratibha I would like to thank Cherry Smyth for lending her newspaper clippings, Nasreen Memon, Ros Pendelbury and Jean Carlomusto for reading the manuscript and for their suggestions, Penny Ashbrook for the loan of Channel 4's *OUT* coverage of the 1992 International AIDS Conference in Amsterdam and Mark Hayduck for transcribing. I would also like to thank my friends and family on both sides of the Atlantic for their love and support: June, Sherin, Kerin, Gita, Sunita, Imani, Sanaxe, Shaffiqu, Robert, Mike, Isaac, Jane. Finally, I want to thank and acknowledge Shaheen Haq, my partner of over a decade, who demands the highest from me, gives the most and remains my closest collaborator in life.

About the authors

Sue O'Sullivan and **Pratibha Parmar** have worked together since 1985 when they were both at Sheba Feminist Press. They have collaborated on several writing projects and remain friends across continents.

Sue O'Sullivan has taught women-and-health classes for over fifteen years and has edited a number of books on health and sexuality. She has been concerned with AIDS and lesbian sexuality since 1986, when she and Susan Ardill published one of the first serious articles on the subject specifically addressed to women. She has spoken to many women's and lesbian groups about HIV and AIDS and sexuality and has been particularly keen on facilitating discussions bringing together women's experiences and feelings about sex with HIV/AIDS education. She co-edited, with Kate Thomson, *Postively Women: Living with AIDS* (Sheba Feminist Publishers, 1992). She is currently living in Australia.

Pratibha Parmar is a writer and independent video-and film-maker. She has taught courses on women, race and culture and has written on race, representation and gender. In 1988 she made a video called *Reframing AIDS,* which challenged dominant representations of the AIDS crisis and created a forum for some of the leading activists in the field to discuss the issues and debates as they affected the lesbian and gay communities. Since then she has made numerous videotapes and films for broadcast television, including *Khush* (*OUT*, 1991) an award-wining film about South Asian lesbians and gay men, *A Place of Rage* (1991) about Angela Davis, June Jordan and Alice Walker, and *Double the Trouble Twice the Fun* (*OUT*, 1992) a short film about lesbians and gay men with disabilities.

Beth Zemsky is a psychotherapist, educator and community organizer. She is currently the training and consultation co-ordinator for the Gay and Lesbian Community Action Council, Minneapolis, Minnesota, US.

Contributors

Jean Carlomusto Gay Men's Health Crisis Project worker, New York
Da Choong Women's development officer, Terrence Higgins Trust
Teresa Edmans HIV/AIDS co-ordinator, London Borough of Islington
Casey Galloway Housing worker, Blackliners
Robin Gorna Terrence Higgins Trust volunteer
Jenny Harrison Blackliners worker
Amber Hollibaugh Director, Lesbian AIDS Project, New York
Joyce Hunter President, National Lesbian and Gay Foundation, US
Hope Massiah Training officer, Positively Women
Nasreen Memon Freelance publicist living in London
Madhu Asian lesbian living in London
Sandy Nelson Health advisor, Sandra Bernhard Clinic

Preface

When American AIDS activist Maxine Wolfe raised the issue of woman-to-woman transmission of HIV with a US government official, he replied *'Do lesbians have sex?'* (Maxine Wolfe, *Lesbian London*, Issue 4, April 1992). That kind of response, joking or not, does not inspire confidence that lesbians' relation to HIV and AIDS is of much interest to the big boys. So who else except lesbians themselves will make sure that any questions at all are raised? Who else will ensure that lesbians are put on HIV agendas, even as an addendum?

This book comes out of our long-term interest in lesbian sexuality and HIV and AIDS. We felt there was a big gap in discussions on these issues that publishing a new set of safer-sex guidelines would not fill. Our priority was to pull together debates, arguments and explorations of both lesbian sexuality and HIV and AIDS, in the belief that we can only take on safer sex or make meaningful decisions about whether or not to practise it once we have begun to talk about our sexual lives with more freedom and honesty and are fully aware of the available information and facts. We are not trying to put forward a competing view on lesbians and HIV and AIDS in these pages – one that claims the most morally and medically correct position. We would prefer to let go of the whole notion of a hierarchy of correctness: no one moves forward or makes lasting changes in her life because of commands.

As we finish writing this book, levels of controversy and argument about lesbians and HIV and AIDS are rising and lesbians are responding to the continuing AIDS crisis in different ways. In the period of approximately six years since safer sex for lesbians found its way on to the agenda, we have seen the emergence of a belief that lesbians are at risk from HIV transmission through woman-to-woman sex; a growing amount of literature which includes safer-sex guidelines for lesbians; even the inclusion of lesbians in the general exhortation that *everyone* engaged in sexual encounters use safer sex. Yet in Britain today, most lesbians know no HIV-positive lesbians, and almost certainly no one who says that woman-to-woman sex was her only possible route of infection. So for large sections of different lesbian communities, safer-sex orthodoxy is seen as irrelevant, even if it has brought up questions, dilemmas, and the possibility of more open sex talk. There are lesbians who believe we are not at risk from HIV because of our 'natural' superiority to heterosexuals, and to men. These lesbians have no interest, beyond polite compassion, in HIV, except as something to keep out of the lesbian community (sic). We are completely critical of this position. Then there are lesbians who believe that only 'bad' lesbians with guilty secrets – women they would immediately recognize and avoid as sexual partners – could be positive, a position we strongly challenge. And finally, there are those who do not believe lesbian sex to be a risk activity. How are we to make sense of these contradictory viewpoints?

AIDS is one of the most devastating occurrences in the world today and will continue to wreak havoc for many years to come. We want more urgent and forceful action to challenge the epidemic wherever it manifests itself. We want those people who are excluded from or marginalized within current research and debates to be given respect – which includes proper resources and scientific enquiry into their specific relationship to AIDS. These people include women, gay men, and people in the African, Asian and other 'third-world' countries affected by AIDS. Lesbians who are HIV positive exist, both within and outside lesbian communities, and it is up to all of us to make these women feel less isolated, to enable them to come out and be supported, if they wish.

In spring 1992, a conference on feminism and HIV and AIDS in Bristol was cancelled because so few women registered for it. Of the few who did, almost all worked in HIV/AIDS organizations. The organizers had targetted women in higher education, yet had received no response. It is shocking to us that this could happen in 1992. **This book is a challenge to complacency and indifference!**

Lesbians and HIV: what's it all about?

Lesbians and HIV. Lesbians and AIDS. Lesbians and safer sex. Protection: from what? from whom? Latex, dental dams, clingfilm, latex gloves, periods, wetness, vaginal secretions. Sucking, fucking, feeling fingers, tongues, mouths. Sex toys, desire, arseholes, breasts, feather-light, soft, SM. Lust, orgasms. Love, monogamy, non-monogamy. Certainty, ambivalences. What makes a lesbian? What else is a lesbian besides her desire for another woman? Can lesbians fuck men? Do they hate men? Are they separatists? Motorcyclists? Teachers? Queers? Babies, butches, femmes, feminists, political dykes, inclusive, exclusive? Are they black, white, of colour, equal, old, young, disabled? Rich, poor, getting by?

- *If god wanted to punish homosexuals, why is lesbian sex the safest sex possible?*
- *Lesbian sex is not safe*
- *Lesbians don't need to use latex for fucking or sucking*
- *Lesbian energy is being drained by gay men and the issue of HIV*
- *HIV is about lesbian lives*

What comes first? Lesbianism? IV drug use? Prostitution? Politics? Labels? Children? Resistance? Acceptance? Denial? Celebration? Politics, health, class, race – whose politically correct line? Who is politically correct anyway? Connections, divisions, diversity, coalitions. Invisibility, belonging, death, bigotry, denial.

At the beginning of this health crisis, in the first part of the 80s, our placement as lesbians seemed peripheral. Marginalized and invisible within the straight world, however strong in our subcultures, the majority of lesbians in the UK, US and other western countries understood themselves to be also (thankfully) outside the AIDS crisis, looking in, or averting their eyes. But soon a shift was taking place: *We may not be in any real danger through our sexual practices, but we do more with our time than have sex!* Lesbians are not all women who have never had sex with men, or never will; who have never injected drugs, or never will; who have never been raped, or never will be; who had no blood transfusions before 1985 (when blood and blood products started to be screened for HIV); who had never self-inseminated with sperm from an untested donor. There is no single, pure definition of what a *real* lesbian is, let alone what *real* lesbian sex is.

It may be difficult for lesbians to discuss being positive because of the idea that it is your lesbian identity that defines you – to admit you had sex with a man or that you are, or have been, an IV drug user goes against what is generally acceptable within the community. If you say you had sex with a man five or six years ago, that may be accepted by a potential woman partner, but if you say you still do now and then, that could be difficult to talk about. There may be groups within the lesbian community who are open with each other about taking drugs, but in my experience, if someone comes out and says she uses IV drugs, a lot of women wouldn't want to hear about it. Da Choong

In fact, lesbians *were* personally involved in the AIDS epidemic because they were everywhere (more or less), and identifying as a lesbian or having woman-to-woman sex didn't negate or subsume other parts of their lives. Who was being excluded when it was avowed that lesbians weren't affected? Who was managing to say, *It couldn't happen to me because I'm a lesbian* only by repressing other aspects of their lives, like occasionally fucking with men? Who was being scared out of talking about those other aspects, past and present? How many were defining lesbianism as membership of certain communities or subcultures? Too many.

At the same time, many lesbians, especially in the US, were joining groups, made up primarily of gay men, to organize around HIV and AIDS. Some of these were activist in orientation, others supportive. Lesbians joined the fight out of compassion, solidarity, the link they saw between gay men and lesbians, and political concern. And then people affected by HIV and AIDS other than gay men were surfacing in growing numbers, too. More and more women were identified as HIV positive, most often heterosexual in practice, and often living in cities like Edinburgh (where the combination of IV drug use and a repressive police force that outlawed fresh-needle supply schemes was apparent), or New York City, where women were becoming positive through heterosexual sex or IV drug use. These women were, and still are, overwhelmingly poor and of colour.

That more women were being discovered to be HIV positive was uncontested. However, the way they were viewed or addressed was often problematic, to say the least. They were usually labelled as pathetic victims or as vectors of disease, or both. Sexism, never far from the fore, arrived on the heels of homophobia – and it showed itself in society, in the medical and scientific professions, and even in AIDS organizations themselves.

Defining the scapegoat

The AIDS crisis has been with us for over a decade. It is not going to go away. At first, in the US and Europe, it was perceived as a gay epidemic (ironically this often meant that straight people assumed lesbians to be part of the 'high-risk group'). But since then, it's also been characterized as an

African problem, often with the direct hypothesis that the virus originated in Africa and therefore Africa is to blame. Racism is as much to the fore as sexism and homophobia within the AIDS discourse.

Laterally, HIV was characterized as affecting particular groups of people, be they IV drug users, bisexuals, gays, prostitutes, Haitians, poor American women of colour, or promiscuous sluts. In every case, the mainstream tendency has been to assign the appearance of HIV within a particular group to the group identity, rather than to activities some members of that group might partake in. Therefore much advice on how to avoid AIDS has been focused, sometimes through innuendo, on shunning people seen as 'infected' by virtue of their identity: *don't sleep with Africans, avoid bisexuals, be suspicious of prostitutes, blame gays, watch out for dirty women.*

Inevitably such groups are placed outside the norm: they are 'other'. Often the facts concerning the supposedly contaminated groups are woefully wrong: for example, large numbers of prostitutes in the UK are extremely knowledgable about safer-sex techniques. And prostitutes tell, with stunning similarity, stories of Johns who will pay extra to fuck without a condom.

Most newspaper and television reporting leaves the public frightened but reinforced in the view that AIDS is something that happens to marginalized groups other than themselves. Of course, there have been attempts by government and voluntary organizations and health educators to involve everyone in taking on board the possibility that they too could be at risk (it's not 'just' gays, folks). But popular discourse remains weighted towards projecting anxieties outwards, so that people who think of themselves as 'normal' can dismiss any anxiety about their own risk through fear and loathing of someone else.

In 1991, one of us gave a lecture on gays and lesbians, the media, and HIV to a group of sixteen- to eighteen-year-olds at a boys' public school. After carefully breaking down the myths, sympathetically addressing their possible fears, and explaining the facts (as they are known), she opened up the discussion. Silence. Until one boy stood up and said the talk should have been presented to a less sophisticated group. More silence. She asked if anyone could articulate their own fears about AIDS. Silence. Until another boy, still sitting, head down, shouted out: *'GAYS!'* No one objected. He could easily have said, blacks, or drug addicts. The circle of prejudice, denial and projection was unbroken.

When AIDS first became the terrible gay plague, I was knifed sixty times because of the graffiti all over the place, which was *Kill a Gay, rid the world of AIDS.* I became disabled because of the history of the lesbian and gay movement. Kate Brown, 'Double the Trouble Twice the Fun' ('OUT' television documentary, 1992)

Where the money goes

Women have been largely invisible within AIDS discourse, or, if seen, have been subject to relative indifference, misinformation, or dismissed as being of minor importance in themselves. What interest there is focuses on women as mothers and on how a positive status might affect a foetus.

A glaring illustration of this state of affairs is the lack of attention paid to the ways HIV is transmitted to (and from) women, and the way illnesses associated with HIV may develop in a woman who is positive. The invisibility or lack of interest in the specificities of women's physiology and biology in this area is staggering. Diseases such as pelvic inflammatory disease (PID), chlamydia, other vaginal infections and cervical cancer are all conditions which are dangerous for positive women and whose presence may indicate a positive status or an acceleration of immunosuppression. They need to be recognized and treated as such. They are also not counted in the long list of HIV-associated opportunistic illnesses which are used officially to give someone who is positive an AIDS diagnosis. As well as affecting treatment, an AIDS diagnosis may mean that a person is entitled to extra benefits, for instance, to be considered a priority for housing. As women, lesbians suffer all these attitudes; if they have the nerve to come out, their lesbianism is an added problem to the medical profession and the social services.

There is no escaping that HIV and AIDS implode most destructively on those people who may be engaging in unsafe behaviour and who are already oppressed, exploited, and/or marginalized by society. So, of course, do other conditions, such as cancer, heart disease and chronic illness. People who are poor have less access to the necessities of daily life, less access to services, including the health service, and are often seen as inherently sickly or as wilful agents of their own illnesses. (*Why do all those women on the dole/welfare smoke so much? They should be using their money to buy better food.*) Stress, bad work conditions or no work, and lack of money to buy the trappings of healthy living, including decent housing, place those at the bottom of the economic heap more at risk from most of the diseases and health-affecting conditions of the twentieth century.

Before the AIDS epidemic, middle-class gay men were not especially subject to life-threatening or out-of-control diseases or conditions. They were in danger from discrimination, hatred, and too often queer-bashing, but on the whole they had enough money and access to services to take care of the sexual health conditions associated with homosexuality. So the large group of mainly white, vaguely middle- or lower-middle-class gay men suffered no more generalized poor health than a comparable group of straight men.

When AIDS occurred so destructively in gay men, it was undoubtedly their homosexuality which rendered them relatively unimportant, or even expendable, in the eyes of the government and health and social services, and delayed much-needed official funding, research and provision of care. At the same time, it was their collective gay identity that enabled such an amazing community response to the crisis. Finally, the fact that they were men, albeit deviant men, meant that a significant number of them had access to some money and to positions of relative power.

The caring sex

Historically and currently, women are placed differently to men in relation to health, be it their own, their children's, their family's. There is no biological justification for the way women are placed socially as carers, but the gender-specific hold of the concept is nonetheless terrible and strong. The mixed feelings that batter women when they take care of other people's health needs, be they as basic as food preparation and clean up, taking toddlers to the doctor, or caring for sick parents or brothers and sisters, are legion. Caring is often an expression of love and feelings of responsibility. But when caring is assumed to be a natural attribute and is expected, at the expense of the development of other human attributes, it can become a mighty burden.

Women, even lesbians, were raised to be caregivers in general and caregivers to men in particular. And even though lesbians have made a conscious choice to disown that heritage, we have nonetheless incorporated many of its basic tenets.
Jackie Winnow, 'Lesbians Evolving Health Care: Cancer and AIDS'

Traditionally, women have put off dealing with their own health problems if they are overwhelmed with caring for others. And doctors have brushed them aside if they complain about vaginal infections, stress, generalized abdominal discomfort, or exhaustion. Some women identified as HIV positive or diagnosed with AIDS die faster than men do. Does the virus work its way more destructively in these women than in men? We don't know yet because not enough research is focused on women. Does the virus have worse effects on many women because they are disadvantaged as women, and doubly so if they are black or poor? Do poor HIV-positive women in the US die sooner because there is not even a semblance of a National Health Service in that country, and is the situation different in Britain, where at least there is still a baseline of medical treatment and care for all? We can extrapolate from our knowledge of other health-threatening conditions or diseases and say *yes* to all these questions.

Bodies with histories

HIV and AIDS is a relatively new phenomenon. But the virus is not operating in a void, within neutral bodies. The virus is present in bodies with histories, with different cultures, and with different economic power, all of which influence the course it takes. The virus has no conscious aim; it doesn't choose particular people because of who they are. Its entry point is through certain behaviours. It isn't sex itself, or IV drug use itself, which is a danger in relation to HIV. Someone who always uses clean needles is not at risk. Someone who fucks vaginally or anally always using a condom reduces their risk greatly.

We are dealing with an epidemic which, by luck of the draw and by virtue of the different kinds of powerlessness, exploitation, invisibility and marginalization of the major groups affected, has impacted more harshly and tragically than it need have done. To intervene has required huge amounts of anger, political energy, creativity and passion – and the task continues. In such a situation, there is no way lesbians can be outside, looking on indifferently, without being challenged. Whether or not we as lesbians can transmit HIV through sex is not the crux of whether or not we are or should be involved in AIDS work, activism, research, or safer-sex talks. What follows are some lesbian responses to some of the issues AIDS and HIV have raised.

HIV debates

Is woman-to-woman transmission possible?

As so little is known about woman-to-woman transmission, lesbians are forced to make their own judgments. It is not surprising, therefore, that strong disagreements and deep divisions exist between women about whether transmission is possible or probable. What seems important to remember is that these are disagreements between lesbians who all care about women, and who are equally involved in AIDS work and/or activism. In this section we have given a platform to different voices and opinions about the current state of affairs.

What do they mean by woman-to-woman transmission? I travel all over America and meet thousands of lesbians of every geographic location, class, race, and I have never met a woman who told me she got HIV from another woman. I know about six lesbians who've died of AIDS that they contracted from IV drug use, and although they weren't practising safer sex, their lovers did not get the virus from them. There are cases of women who've got syphilis from their HIV+ lovers, but not HIV. So anecdotally, it appears that HIV is not sexually transmitted between women. Sarah Schulman, AIDS activist, interview in 'Capital Gay ', 29 November 1991

We see woman-to-woman transmission. The numbers are small, that is true... but just because there aren't the numbers doesn't mean it isn't happening. Rita Shimmin, HIV program co-ordinator, Lyon-Martin Women's Health Services, San Francisco in Nancy Solomon, 'Risky Business: Should lesbians practise safer sex?'

Barbara Adler, an education and counselling co-ordinator for San Francisco's AIDS Health Project, knows lesbians who are HIV positive and also believes the virus can be spread through sexual contact between women.

We know that blood carries the virus and women bleed every month.
Adler in Solomon, ibid

But while Adler speaks from limited personal experience, it would appear that this is one area in which researchers agree among themselves and tend to disagree with her:

Researchers agree that menstrual blood does not carry the virus in the same potency as circulatory blood, which has a higher living cell density than other body fluids. The only published report on HIV transmission during menses (Annals of Internal Medicine, 1987) found traces of HIV in cervical secretions of four of the seven HIV-positive women in the study. A large-scale study on menses has yet to be published, so the level of HIV in menstrual blood remains unknown. Nancy Solomon, ibid

The issue is complicated by the impossibility of knowing how a lesbian (or anyone else) identified as HIV positive contracted the virus.

Most doctors know very little about what lesbians do sexually, so they are unlikely to ask about the range of sexual practices that may have occurred, such as sharing sex toys. Given the hierarchical way routes of transmission are decided – for women, IV drug use comes first and then heterosexual contact – any woman who has had sex with a man in the last ten years, or had a blood transfusion before 1985, would automatically be put under one of those categories, rather than woman-to-woman transmission, even if it was clear that her partner had HIV as well. Da Choong

There are many doctors and government-sponsored researchers who say lesbian sexual transmission is virtually non-existent. They point out other significant risks in the cases attributed to woman-to-woman transmission. They say it's impossible to depend on patients to truthfully disclose how they were exposed to HIV. Nancy Solomon, ibid

An out lesbian might find it easier to talk about lesbian sexual behaviour than a drug or alcohol history; she might be unwilling to talk about heterosexual contacts; she could have memory blackouts from drug or alcohol use. Sarah Schulman in Solomon, ibid

The Centers for Disease Control (a US government agency that tracks AIDS) has to date identified no high-risk sexual behaviour between women and finds no reason to believe that lesbians are a risk group. The CDC defines a lesbian as a woman who has reported 'sex relations exclusively with females since 1977'. The CDC uses a hierarchy of categories to determine HIV-transmission data: female-to-female transmission is not used as a possible exposure category. But the percentage of cases among women that have been placed in the 'no identified risk' category is double that of men, indicating how much less is known.

Along with many other official bodies, the CDC is notorious for its lack of research on HIV and AIDS in women: to date, there have been no clinical trials carried out on women to see how the virus may or may not manifest itself differently. Since when can we as women trust government or medical institutions which historically have been known to marginalize our health needs?

There's almost no information and what there is is almost all anecdotal. I do see lesbians with HIV, and some consider their primary risk to have been sexual transmission from a woman. But they are often caught in a contradiction. For example, they may have a partner who is HIV positive and they have been with that woman for three years and had regular sex with her. They have also fucked one man twice in three years. In the scientific community, their only risk would be considered the sex with the man, though the women themselves consider the risk much more likely to be their three years with their ongoing female partner. These women are completely discredited – in the lesbian community because they had sex with a man, and in the scientific community because there's considered no risk for lesbians. We know very little and we have to begin really to compare information and not compete for the right message. Amber Hollibaugh

When we consider lesbians and HIV and AIDS, we are struck by the lack of a story or collection of stories to make sense of it all. Whom do we believe? Do we invent scenarios to fit our expectations and pre-existing plot lines? What are our needs in relation to others? What is our stake in AIDS militancy, the AIDS industry?

Many lesbians distance themselves from HIV. They don't think they know anyone who is HIV positive. They don't think it's an issue in the community, so there isn't space for lesbians who are positive to talk about it openly. It's a cycle we have to break out of. Da Choong

Safer sex or not?

Calls for all lesbians to practise safer sex, accompanied by lists of practices with assignments of risk – always with dental dams (or cut-up condoms), surgical gloves and nonoxynol-9 named as the practical means of protection – have probably created as much confusion and fear about AIDS as they have opened up a wider discussion of the subject. It's a classic case of a 'health-education' message which is prescriptive and bossy and, because it doesn't resonate in daily life, raises anxieties and confusions and is then blocked out by individuals in their practice. Giving information is not necessarily creating empowerment. For that to happen, the information has to make sense and there has to be a critical yet flexible framework to help individuals and communities to evaluate it and to distinguish what is important and relevant within the overload thrown at them. For example, safer-sex advice for heterosexuals rarely, if ever, tells men or women to use dental dams when practising cunnilingus. Are male heterosexual tongues different from women's?

I think there is an alarmist attitude. You don't always have to use dental dams or condoms. I think latex should be incorporated into the bedroom

but I don't think it should be the law.
Imani Harrington, HIV-positive poet and dancer, in Solomon, ibid

Dental dams have been recommended by those of us who think we need to practise safer sex as lesbians. But they are not a good form of safer sex: they are very hard to use, they are inefficient and expensive, and there's been no scientific research. Amber Hollibaugh

From the early years of the epidemic, when lesbians tended to wax lyrical about the safeness of lesbian sex, to the later period of assertions about the necessity of safer sex for everyone, to the present point of fracture and disagreement, there has never been a collective sense of what HIV means for lesbians. Today, some are saying that safer sex for lesbians is a red herring: it detracts from the real ways lesbians are affected by HIV and obscures the need for safer-sex education and practice in the communities and groups who are really at risk. Others say this position is irresponsible: no one knows for sure if the virus can be transmitted by oral sex, for instance, and it is better to be safe than sorry. Still others, including some positive lesbians, are convinced that lesbian sexual transmission has already happened and may happen more if lesbians don't practise safer sex now.

The most recent controversy was sparked off by advertisements and posters issued by UK AIDS charity, the Terrence Higgins Trust. These tell lesbians they are:

- *[at] very low risk in oral sex*
- *...so ditch those dental dams*
- *don't bother with gloves unless it turns you on*
- *if you share sex toys, use condoms.*

In smaller type, it reads:

However, lesbians have been infected with HIV through sharing 'works', sex with men and donor insemination.

The THT stand at the 8th International AIDS Conference in Amsterdam in 1992 was zapped by many extremely angry lesbians, particularly from the US. Below we present some of the views both supporting the campaign and against it. The lesbian community is far from homogeneous, and these voices highlight some of the different positions on the need, or not, for lesbian safer-sex practices.

The THT advertising campaign was especially aimed at updating lesbians on the relative risks of HIV infection in lesbian sex. This campaign was launched in conjunction with the second edition of our leaflet, 'HIV and AIDS – Information for Lesbians', which incorporates new guidelines on safer sex for lesbians. Our purpose was to present a balanced view based on the latest research and from a health-education approach of risk reduction rather than risk elimination. Da Choong

The reason behind this campaign is the need for more intellectual honesty about the risk of transmission. And the fact is that we have no consistent evidence of transmission through cunnilingus. Look at the history of the way we have done safer-sex education. Back in the early 80s we told gay men, be careful about kissing, we told them, no sucking, no fucking. Now we are moving the message on, we are saying, yes, have anal sex but use condoms and lubricants, yes, fellatio is OK, you might not want to come in another man's mouth, but it's not even much of a risk if you do. That's the shift we are seeing in lesbian safer sex too. Robin Gorna, THT volunteer

When I saw the THT posters I was floored. I think it is totally unethical. We don't have enough information one way or another to know about woman-to-woman transmission. Nobody is doing any studies and this ad is a terrible mistake because it makes the wrong assumption that lesbians are not at risk. Joyce Hunter

I think the advert is irresponsible. They stated in a letter to Capital Gay *(19 July 1992) that the purpose of the campaign was to generate a debate, but this is not a good way to go about it. Already there are too many lesbians who don't think that HIV is an issue and when they see THT, a reputable organization, put out such information it will reinforce this denial.* Madhu

To whom are we talking when we speak about safer sex for lesbians? If an HIV-positive lesbian is trying to figure out how to conduct her sex life, how can we advise her to throw away her dental dams? In the absence of research which proves whether HIV can, or cannot, be transmitted sexually from woman to woman, latex gloves and dams may play a crucial role in helping an HIV-positive lesbian to feel secure enough to have sex again. The point is that there are lesbians with HIV/AIDS and they should not be rendered invisible when considering services or educational materials. Jean Carlomusto

What use would the ad/poster advice be to a menstruating ex-heroin user into fisting or anal sex? Just look at how far we still have to go in halting the spread of the virus in gay men, many of whom never had the choice of knowing about how to protect themselves. In the absence of serious research, should safer sexual practices between women really only be taken on board once evidence ends up showing low risk becoming higher? Nasreen Memon

In the absence of final answers, there are few people prepared to say they are 100 per cent certain that lesbians cannot transmit HIV through woman-to-woman sex. That would be a scary thing to do. However, the ways in which you weigh up risk in your own life, or more collectively how you and your friends, lovers or peer groups do that, is difficult, but not impossible. Low risk may not mean no risk at all, but how we respond to that reality will differ from woman to woman and community to community, as it does with many other life-affecting behaviours.

We know a number of lesbians are HIV positive already, and it is important to find ways of allowing them to be part of whatever lesbian community they choose. Unfortunately, ignorance and/or bigotry do exist in our communities and need to be confronted.

A few months ago I spoke to a lesbian who became infected and she was saying her confidentiality was breached and it became known in the lesbian community. She used to go to a coffee shop and when they found out they broke the cups and plates she had used and barred her from going there again because of their fear of infection. Subsequently they were spoken to and she is now allowed to use the coffee shop, but only on the understanding that she uses disposable and this is 1992. I don't think the lesbian community is prepared to deal with this.
Teresa Edmans

Lesbians need to step outside the political dialogue about sexuality and understand that HIV is a pressing issue for many, many lesbians. As long as that's true, we need not to abandon other lesbians who are HIV positive.
Amber Hollibaugh

Lesbians, AIDS and other issues

From the very early days of the AIDS crisis, many lesbians have responded with urgency and action. Lesbians have gained enormous experience in the women's health movement, specifically through campaigns about abortion rights, artificial insemination and enforced sterilization, and have used this experience to help build a model of social response to the crisis. Many feel that the lessons learned in fighting AIDS could now be applied to life-threatening conditions that effect women specifically, and that this isn't happening quickly enough.

I am both a cancer activist and an AIDS activist. As a lesbian feminist, I have been involved with the AIDS crisis since the early 1980s. In 1985 I was diagnosed with breast cancer, founded the Women's Cancer Resource Center in Berkeley, California in 1986, and was diagnosed with metastatic breast cancer in my lungs and bones in 1988. I have lost friends, acquaintances and colleagues to cancer and to AIDS. Both of these diseases are life-threatening, and yet I have seen my community rally around one and overlook the other.
Jackie Winnow, 'Lesbians Evolving Health Care: Cancer and AIDS'

Breast cancer and cervical cancer kill many, many, more women than HIV in Europe and the US. And this will be true for the foreseeable future. Why aren't we lobbying and working around these issues on the same level as around HIV and AIDS? There's no health-prevention work on a similar scale for either breast or cervical cancer. And cervical cancer is known to be sex-related. Da Choong

Our point in drawing attention to this debate is not to pit one struggle against another. Lesbians need to be aware of how groups facing different health crises can be played off against one another.

This inequality is not the fault of the people with AIDS, but rather of the systems that create the divisions. People start fighting over the same piece of the pie. It is not an accident. Jackie Winnow, ibid

Many lesbians who have been active over a long period around issues like rape and abortion find it hard to see how in ten short years the provisions for HIV and AIDS work and prevention have mushroomed with resources, when women's health issues have never received that level of funding. I can sympathize with that... If HIV and AIDS had initially affected lesbians, it probably wouldn't have the high profile it has now. Da Choong

Some gay men, too, are expressing disquiet at what they see as inappropriate lesbian responses to HIV and AIDS. At a certain point in the AIDS crisis there was a swing away from a gay focus. Wherever this came from – sometimes from mainstream government policy-makers, who saw gay men as an unpopular target for public funding; sometimes from gay organizations themselves, who wished to weaken the link between AIDS and homosexuality – the message going out began to focus on the risk of HIV to *everyone*. Worldwide, 60 per cent of those affected by HIV were heterosexual. That meant that safer-sex messages were for everyone.

The 'everyone is affected' health-education slant has recently been criticized by gay men, who have became more and more invisible within the messages. The extent to which this is now the case in the UK is revealed in a report published in August 1992 by the North West Thames Regional Health Authority, which concludes that three-quarters of AIDS and HIV organizations in Britain, the majority funded by the National Health Service or local authorities, are failing to provide safer-sex messages for gay men. Of the 226 agencies researched, 169 were giving no advice to gay men about risks of transmission. When asked why they omitted to target gay men, 14 said they believed there were none in their district, 16 said there was managerial opposition to such projects, 41 said they did not know how to contact homosexual men. One district co-ordinator asserted:

We have no homosexual community here: you might try district X, they have a theatre. 'Independent', 13 August 1992

Clearly *everyone* isn't everyone in terms of resources and the AIDS industry.

Yet in what appears an almost classic case of attacking the people nearest to you rather than your real enemies, some gay men are now claiming that lesbians working in HIV and AIDS are taking up valuable resources at a point where gay men continue to be the main group affected in Britain and other northern European countries. Within this scenario, lesbians are criticized simply for pointing out the lack of knowledge about women and HIV – a stance that provoked some acrimonious exchanges at the 1992 International AIDS Conference in Amsterdam.

For the first time, here at this conference, I have heard gay men talk about *virus envy*. Come on! We can't be competitive, we need to be there for each other and the boys need to remember that the lesbians were there for them. Joyce Hunter

Lesbians who agree that gay men need ongoing support and more resources are being put in the tedious position of having to explain that lesbians and gay men working together successfully and with realistic objectives does not mean subsuming all other issues. Some of these may pre-date the AIDS crisis and remain unresolved – after all, lesbians and gay men have not always worked together unproblematically. While we do not need to fight AIDS through a hierarchy of oppression, the virtual absence of lesbian groups and political organizations is a serious problem. Has lesbian involvement in AIDS activism and services had an adverse effect on lesbian political organizations?

There is certainly a political view that why should lesbians help gay men anyway, because would they do the same if things were reversed? Would they come and support lesbians, and god haven't we supported men all our lives, and here we are again being required to support men? Teresa Edmans

Race against AIDS?

AIDS has dramatically affected the populations of the countries of Asia, in particular India, Thailand, Burma and China, and of Africa, especially Ethiopia, Uganda, Kenya and Zimbabwe. At the time of writing, there were an estimated 10 to 12 million adults in these countries infected with HIV and between 1 and 2 million children, with an estimated 1 million new infections in the last six months of 1992 (one person every fifteen to twenty seconds). Over half of new infections are in women. Yet the rampant spread of the virus in these countries and lack of resources for prevention and treatment, exacerbated in many cases by 'first-world' economic policies, has largely been ignored.

Closer to home, however, the idea of Africans as potential 'carriers of the plague' has been widespread, and government media campaigns and services have treated people of colour in ways determined by racist perceptions from the beginning of the crisis. As far back as 1987, many black lesbians and gay men experienced increased government surveillance and police harassment, while Africans visiting Britain were subject to immigration nightmares. The level of misinformation that still exists is illustrated by the recent reaction experienced by a worker for Blackliners, a London-based organization for black and Asian people with HIV and AIDS, when she tried to give blood.

I was handed a leaflet which listed people who should not give blood. It included those who had just returned from holiday in Africa or had slept with an African since 1977. The feeling that black people are to blame still exists. Jenny Harrison

Most significant clinical drug trials have to date been carried out only on white men, so it is difficult to assess the effectiveness of drugs such as AZT on women or on members of other racial groups. And much of the information produced assumes its readers to be white – for example in describing the appearance of skin cancer Kaposi's Sarcoma (KS) only on white skin.

I used to work at Frontliners, which predominantly served white, gay men. I was very impressed by the PWAs (People with AIDS), who were fully aware of their medical history, medication and its effects. The black people I'm seeing now are not as in control of what's being given to them. They are much more disempowered. Casey Galloway

I think that there is often covert racism in many HIV organizations and services. The concerns of many African women about their legal status are very real. Issues of immigration and/or refugee status are seen as side issues by these organizations, but these are intrinsically to do with you as a whole person. Many times such women seeking counselling on HIV and AIDS are made to feel they are a special case, a burden. They are made to feel grateful for what is their basic right. Hope Massiah

Many of the divisions and fragmentations that have surfaced within queer communities have been duplicated within AIDS activism.

The hierarchies of oppression are alive and well in AIDS work. Black people often have to cut off different parts of themselves, like put up with racism in a white organization just to get support. Hope Massiah

As HIV and AIDS continue to affect all communities, it is imperative to work on more than one front at a time. When setting our agendas we must remember the situation of all the people already affected by the virus. Throwing out a politics moralistically built on a hierarchy of oppression does not mean denying a politics which takes into account who is most affected by HIV and AIDS or who gets the worst deal if they are positive.

It is our strong belief that even if lesbians were magically immune from HIV transmission by virtue of their lesbianism, we would still be asserting the importance of lesbian involvement in and understanding of the politics of HIV and AIDS, and of their agitating with others to end the AIDS crisis and to meet the needs of those who are already positive or ill. This would not be out of the goodness of our lesbian hearts: it would be because a separatism based on whether or not a particular issue affects *you* directly is politically shortsighted and ultimately reactionary.

And in any case, magically immune lesbians would still be affected by HIV and AIDS. The epidemic exists and the link between some forms of sex and transmission has changed the face of the ongoing battles about sex and sexuality. Face it: deviancy is part of most of these discussions, and what are lesbians if not part of the sexually deviant world?

What's going down?

Beth Zemsky

The title for this chapter comes from the title of a workshop I lead for lesbians about sex. I chose it because I liked the squirming it produced, the visual image it left me, and the variety of meanings it conveys. Runner-up titles included: 'Lips, clits, and latex,' 'Dames and dams', and 'A (gloved) finger in the dyke'. I rejected these partly because I believed them to be too bold for the Midwest of the US (the location of most of the workshops), and partly because my experience indicated that if a workshop appeared to have anything to do with HIV, lesbians would not attend. But if it was advertised to be about sex, they came in droves.

The women at these workshops are hungry to talk about sex. At the beginning, I ask the audience as a group to brainstorm a list of behaviours that signify lesbian sex to them. After much giggling and discomfort, we develop an extensive list: handholding, kissing, fondling, hugging, etc. It is only after significant prompting that behaviours such as cunnilingus, finger-fucking, fisting or anal sex are added to the list. While all the behaviours listed are indeed expressions of lesbian sex, genital sex is almost impossible to mention, even by a group of lesbians who have come together for the explicit purpose of talking about sex. Many women also say they are uncomfortable with the words finally used to describe these behaviours.

Each time I repeat this activity, no matter the location of the workshop, the age of the participants, or their previous experiences of lesbian sex, the audience as a group seems to have the same difficulty describing genital lesbian behaviours.

What's going down here?

In winter 1991, our local Midwest AIDS project published its first pamphlet on lesbians and AIDS. The pamphlet begins with the statement *'most lesbians don't do things that put them at risk of contracting AIDS'*. Who are *most lesbians* and what *things* are we supposedly doing or not doing? And what is *risk*? About these things, the pamphlet is silent.

Silence, invisibility, attempting to view infected lesbians as somehow different, other... eleven years into the epidemic we are still deciding whether HIV/AIDS has anything to do with us.

What's going down here?

It seems that at least part of what's going down is that lesbian sex, in all its forms and in all its diversity, is almost unspeakable. And without a workable discourse concerning lesbian sex, it is almost impossible to have a reasonable discussion about the risk of lesbian sexual transmission of HIV. In this chapter, I will not focus my analysis on whether, based on the available medical research, lesbians *should* practise safer sex. There simply isn't enough research to date to be of much help to us in making this decision. Rather, I choose to focus the discussion on lesbian sex and our expressions of our sexualities. Specifically, I will focus on the things that crowd our beds in addition to the risk of HIV. Also, I suggest that the decision-making methods we already use to determine risk in our sexual encounters can be of service in informing our decisions about risk, sex and exposure to HIV. My hope is to reframe the discussion of lesbian sex and HIV away from a *do* and *don't* rhetoric to a position that celebrates our sexuality and our choices to care for ourselves and our communities even, or perhaps especially, in the face of AIDS.

Speaking lesbian sex

It seems clear from the workshop audiences' reaction to the *'What is lesbian sex?'* exercise that we have a very difficult time verbally describing lesbian sex. (We also have a difficult time defining what is *lesbian*, but that discussion is beyond the scope of what I can cover here.) I believe that we have such a difficult time defining sex and then discussing it in our relationships because of the invisibility of lesbian sex itself. Our culture equates sex with the activity of a penis, and women's sexuality as our experience in relation to that penis. But what happens to sex when the penis is absent? It disappears, from discourses about sex in general, and specifically from AIDS discourse and education. In AIDS discourse, women become wombs that transmit HIV to our 'innocent' children, or vaginas that are seen as vectors of infection transmitting HIV to our unsuspecting (male) partners. Our sexuality drops out of sight, into the dark hole that is the representation of women's bodies.

So we are left with the question: *what is lesbian sex?* While our hands, our tongues, and our cunts may know the answer to this question, can we speak the words in such a way that they have meaning for us? This is and has been difficult for us because we don't have a language, a cultural vernacular, suited to this purpose. This is displayed in the tension present in our discussions about lesbian erotica/pornography, sex toys, SM, and now HIV and safer sex. While all these debates have substantive and crucial points of disagreement, it seems that there are also moments where we simply don't understand each other. I say *penetration*, and you may think *rape*. You say *bondage*, and I may think *violence*. We think we know, but we don't. And we don't even know that we don't know. It is as if sex is written on my body and on your body in indelible inks we cannot decipher.

There have been some attempts to initiate lesbian safer-sex education programmes in the US. However, the assumption of many of these programmes is that we can use the same kind of language and educational approach as has proved successful with gay men. Among the multitude of differences between gay men and lesbians is that before HIV began spreading in gay male communities in the US, the gay male subculture already had a fairly sophisticated sexual culture, including a sexual language, and defined cultural sexual spaces and practices (e.g. handkerchief codes, clothing styles that signified activity preferences, cruising rules and locales). Indeed, rather than the sexual anarchy that mainstream media attempts to portray as the gay male experience of the 70s, gay men as a community had an evolved sexual culture that lent itself to use in the later safer-sex campaigns. For gay men, this wasn't the sudden development of a sexual language; this was a fine tuning of an already well-developed sexual vernacular.

Twenty-three years after Stonewall and eleven years into the epidemic, our task is to continue to develop our own sexual culture, to fill the void ourselves, in part so that it isn't instead filled by mainstream media or the medical establishment. We do have the ability, individually and as a community, to continue to define our sexualities and how we want to practise them. There is a tremendous diversity of lesbian sexual behaviour. No matter what you are into, you are not alone.

The first step in creating a lesbian response to HIV is therefore to talk about what we are doing and what we want – to write, to speak, to wear our sexualities. AIDS activists have used the slogan '*Silence = Death*' to connote the relationship between speech and fighting this disease. For us, speaking is not just about AIDS. It is also, perhaps primarily, about claiming our sexualities. This is not about latex. It is about celebration.

What gets into bed with us?

In almost every discussion about lesbians and HIV in which I've participated, women express fear and resentment about needing to deal with one more thing that impacts on our sexualities. The unanimous feeling seems to be, *don't you think we've had enough already? And now you want us to deal with this too!*

Therefore in any discussion we have about lesbian sex and HIV, it is important to acknowledge that there is a lot that gets into bed with us in addition to the risk of HIV. For many of us, these other issues are much more tangible, and at times much more overwhelming, than the theoretical risk of woman-to-woman sexual transmission of HIV may ever seem.

In the 'What's going down?' workshop, I draw a bed on the blackboard and ask the audience to brainstorm all the things, in addition to our partners, that get into bed with us. The list is unfortunately quite long. Issues that find their way into our beds include: our own or our partner's history of sexual abuse and victimization (and the flashbacks and lack of sexual self-empowerment that often accompanies this experience); unfinished past relationships with lovers; past sexual experience with men (including the expectation of disassociating during sex); transfer time to shake off passing in the heterosexual world; our own or our partner's history of chemical dependency; domestic violence; health issues (e.g. STDs, breast cancer); physical disabilities; issues about our body image; sodomy laws; our lack of basic civil rights; our own or our partner's internalized homophobia; racism; classism; ableism; anti-semitism; ageism; our parents; our kids; our pets; our jobs; our bills; and sometimes our entire lesbian community. Phew!

And, as if this were not enough, other issues that find their way into our beds include differences in sexual scripting and sexual desires; performance anxiety to prove we love being lesbians by being fantastic lovers; premature coupling and incompatibility (the lesbian date-and-mate syndrome); the fusion of sex and love that leads to less erotic tension in our relationships over time; and our socialization as women to be less aggressive and initiative sexually. It is amazing that in beds this crowded, we manage to find each other and be sexual at all.

And now we have to add to these crowded beds the possibility of transmission of HIV. Is it any wonder that we are resistant to the idea of lesbian sexual transmission of HIV and to safer sex? We've had it. We no longer want to have anything new to worry about or to stigmatize our sexuality further. So we argue about numbers and statistical probabilities as a way to keep the possibilities away. However, I believe it is important to break out of the statistical mindset. We ask, *what are the chances*? HIV is present in blood and vaginal fluid, in higher concentration in vaginal fluid in which there is any other infection (including yeast) present. There have been some documented cases of woman-to-woman sexual transmission of HIV.[1] If you or someone you love has AIDS, the impact is 100 per cent.

Yes, our beds are crowded. However, the second step in our response to HIV needs to be at least to acknowledge that in the 90s, whether we like it or not, the possibility of HIV is already in our lives. Even if we decide not to practise safer sex, we still have to think about it. We don't have a choice about this. What we can do is determine how to deal with the possibility of HIV and make decisions about our sexual practices and our relationships in a way that says we, individually and as a community, desire to live and love.

Our calculus of risk

Risk means different things to different people. With our beds as crowded as they are, sex, any kind of sex, has been risky, at times very dangerous – for women and lesbians throughout history. This has, until recently, had nothing to do with the risk of contracting HIV. It has had to do with the lack of control we have had over our bodies. It has had to do with the insidious sexism, racism and homophobia which renders our lives on the one hand invisible and dispensable, and on the other open to invasive government control.

So, sex, lesbian sex, for many of us an integral part of who we are and how we define ourselves, has always taken place in an atmosphere of risk. We have, as individuals and communities, struggled to find a way to negotiate this risk. We have been successful to various degrees. For example, we are finding ways to talk about reproductive choices, sexual violence, lesbian battering, prostitution, and so on, and to negotiate the impact of these on our sexual practices. Therefore the question for me at this juncture is not whether lesbian sex is *safe*, because it never has been. Rather, the question is how we negotiate the new potential risk of sexual transmission of HIV within our existing calculus of risk in our sexual decision-making?

What is important is to shift our perception of risk, or what I call our *proximity of risk*. When we feel closer, more proximate, to something risky, we tend to weigh our decisions differently. Our perception of our current proximity of risk has been affected by the prevailing rhetoric of statistical risk and high-risk groups, the lack of relevant lesbian HIV research, our own desire to protect the small turf of sexual freedom we have carved out for ourselves, and our general difficulty in discussing lesbian sexuality at all. As a community, we seem still to believe that we are very far from risk. However, we are not, and we never have been.

One of the ways we distance ourselves from our own risk is by pretending that only certain kinds of lesbians 'need' practise safer sex. Also, in many communities, stating that you practise safer sex has unfortunately been constructed as an admission of being a member of some 'deviant' lesbian group (e.g. bisexual, drug-using, into SM). This kind of thinking not only leaves us all exposed by mistakenly promoting the idea that only 'those lesbians' are at risk, while 'we' might not be, but it can also lead to the ostracism of those in our communities who might currently be living with HIV. When we hear that someone we know, a lesbian, is HIV positive or symptomatic, do we ask, *how did she get it? What unlesbian thing did she do to become infected?* Obviously, this is blaming the infected person (another version of 'AIDS is god's punishment for queers'), and it is divisive for us as a community. If we can make lesbians who are infected 'other', then we can hold on to the myth that most lesbians do not do things that put them at risk of AIDS.

My point is that it is time to reframe our sense of vulnerability and our sense of sexual celebration as a group, even though individually some of us still don't think that AIDS has anything to do with us. As AIDS writer Cindy Patton has stated:

The question should not be, what have I done to imagine that I should take on the perceived taint of safer sex? Rather, the question is, what am I going to do to empower myself, my sexual partners, my friends to enjoy fulfilling and healthy sex in a society that prefers to treat STDs rather than prevent them, that would just as soon see me dead as design a pamphlet that actually addresses my concerns?[2]

In the 'What's going down?' workshop, I borrow an exercise from AIDS educator Denise Ribble to help the audience rethink their proximity of risk. I ask all the audience to stand, and then to sit down again if they answer *yes* to any of the following questions:

- *Have you had sex since 1977 while your judgment was impaired or you didn't have a choice about your sexual behaviour (e.g. sex under the influence of chemicals, sexual assault, you don't remember sexual behaviours)?*
- *Have you had vaginal or anal intercourse with a man since 1978 without using a condom?*
- *Have you shared needles while using IV drugs or when receiving medical care since 1978?*
- *Have you had a blood transfusion between 1978 and 1985?*
- *Have you had sex with a woman who has had sex with a man without using a condom, had shared needles, has had a blood transfusion, can't remember, or you didn't know?*
- *Have you had vigorous sexual contact with a female partner that caused trauma, e.g. vigorous thrusting with finger or sex toy, being scratched with a hang nail?*
- *Have you been artificially inseminated by a donor whose HIV status is unknown?*

I have done this exercise with hundreds of lesbians in parts of the US that are thought to be low seroprevalence areas. And there have only ever been a few women left standing at the end of the exercise. Sex has always been risky for us, and our risk in relation to HIV is a lot more proximate than we would like to believe. Our response to this risk needs to include consideration of safer sex. Safer sex is not about *do's* and *don'ts,* and it *is* about much more than just latex. It is foremost about making our own informed decisions and assessing our own risks, taking into account all that is risky about sex. We know how to do this. We do this all the time about a myriad of sexual issues.

Safer sex is about figuring out our own and our partners' histories, being honest with ourselves, and remembering that sometimes people lie to get sex. It is about making decisions about behaviours, and/or using latex barriers, based on knowledge. And safer sex is mostly about talking. Practising safer sex can push us to negotiate and communicate more clearly. It reminds us that we *do* have choices about our sexuality and that our sexuality is ours for our health and enjoyment.

Practising safer sex is also about loving ourselves and taking our bodies and our health seriously. Many say, *but we are first learning to love our genitals, our smells, the tastes of our juices. Now you want us to stop. How do we do this and keep loving ourselves?* My answer is to keep loving our genitals, and our smells and our tastes, and to remember that practising safer sex is an expression of love by us for ourselves, our partners and our community. What better way to value our sexuality than to make a choice with every sexual behaviour to affirm our lives. In light of all this, what are a few pieces of latex?

Notes

1. Cases of woman-to-woman sexual transmission of HIV have been documented in a number of sources, including: Marmor, M., Weiss, L. R., Lyden, M. et al (1986) 'Possible female to female transmission of human immunodeficiency virus' (letter), *Annals of Internal Medicine*, 105 (6):969; Monzon, O. T. & Capellan, J. M. B. (1987) 'Female to female transmission of HIV' (letter), *Lancet*, 8549 (2):40-1; Ribble, D. et al (1990) 'HIV infection in lesbians', presented at the 1990 International Conference on AIDS, San Francisco (unpublished)
2. Patton, C. (1989) 'Lesbian safe sex', unpublished

Talking sex: talking serious, talking dirty

As Beth Zemsky and others involved in HIV and AIDS work have pointed out, it's simply not possible to discuss the relation of HIV to lesbians without talking more openly among ourselves about sex. So we have included here our own, exploratory naming of words and of practices which lesbians might or might not do, or know about. It's a start-out, a warm-up, and definitely to be added to.

Lesbian sex is:

- **looking** *at women, at breasts, at eyes, at legs, at mouths, at hair, at clothes, at attitude, at dancing, at working, at play*
- **flirting** *at clubs, with girlfriends, with strangers*
- **holding hands** *on a bus, hidden in coat pockets, on the street, watching television, at a party, meeting parents, going shopping*
- **planning a seduction**
- **hoping to be seduced**
- **undressing** *yourself, another woman, tearing off clothes, taking them off slowly, leaving some on, ripping off a slip, a T-shirt, coming naked into the room, removing underwear under the bedclothes*
- **gazing and longing** *for a long time, for a second or two, not at all*
- **getting down** *in bed, on the floor, in the kitchen, outside, in a dark street, a toilet, your mother's house, over a chair, on your knees, on all fours, on your back, side by side, one on top, head to feet, sitting up, across a table, on your own with a fantasy, together, with others watching, others touching, three or more together, on the beach, in a field, hidden but with people around, at the end of the world, in the water, in a bath, in a car, at a party, a club, a bar, a friend's, your own place, her's, a hotel, a conference*
- **sucking** *nipples, clits, toes, ears, necks, fingers*
- **kissing** *lips, with tongues, open mouths, ears, eyes, all over the body, cunts, arseholes, bellies, bums*
- **hugging** *hard, bearhugs, light ones, group hugs, love hugs*
- **licking** *vulvas, clits, marathon licking, teasing tongue darts, orgasm strokes, skin, arseholes, ears, tongue probing earholes, probing cunts, probing arseholes, licking feet, toes, necks, all over, thighs, fingers*
- **pinching** *nipples, bums, cheeks, with nipple clamps, with fingers, nipping*

with teeth

- **stroking** *all over, backs, breasts, thighs, hair, faces, eyelids, eyebrows*
- **slapping** *bums, faces, cunts*
- **fucking** *finger-fucking the cunt, the arse, the mouth, putting the whole hand in the cunt, in the arsehole, fisting, finding the G-spot and stroke-fucking it, turning fingers in the cunt while fucking, one hand fucking the cunt while the other does the arse, tying her up and teasing her with the fuck to come, fucking with objects*
- **dildoes** *in the cunt, up the arse, held in hands, worn in harnesses, under clothing, for show, used by a partner, on yourself, looking like penises, looking like cylindrical shapes, black, white, pink, shaped like dolphins, corncobs, made out of latex, plastic, wood, rubber, cucumbers, imaginations*
- **butt plugs** *small, medium, long, slim, large, inserted during masturbation, used as a small dildo, left in the arse while making love, fucking the arse with it*
- **lubricants** *for the cunt, for dryness, to make a cunt slippier, for fisting, non-oil-based for using with latex gloves, dental dams, flavoured lubes, plain lubes, always lubes for anal entry, lubes for using on clits for vibrator pleasure*
- **vibrators** *for your own pleasure, for orgasms, for multiple orgasms, for using with a lover, for quickies, for taking on holidays, for using in semi-public places, for pushing against cunts and bums, for fucking with, for easing aching muscles*
- **ejaculation** *some find it cums easily, some don't find the spot, stimulating G-spot with fingers or dildo, bringing yourself or your lover to an ejaculation, in her face, wet the bed*
- **food** *avocadoes, honey, whipped cream, chocolate, grapes, champagne, brandy, salt, lemon juice, mangoes, ice-cream, ice cubes*
- **fingers dancing** *on clits, beside clits, on arseholes, across nipples, on lips, on palms, across backs*
- **fingers moving** *on clits, on tits, in cunts, on bodies*
- **piss** *artists, at orgasm, on someone, golden showers*
- **orgasms** *fast, taking forever, lasting forever, over in seconds, like a sneeze, like an earthquake, one of a number in a row, not worth it, the best thing ever, delicious, exquisite, ordinary, shaking, rolling around, out of control, off into space, rolling along like waves, cute, scarey, makes you cry, makes you laugh, makes you growl, howl, shout, scream, moan, cry out her name, his name, the right name, the wrong name, makes you say the L word, makes you want more, makes you tired, helps period pains, puts you to sleep*
- **do-me queens** *she always gets it and is then too tired*
- **making love** *good sex, bad sex, routine sex, no sex, changing sex, new sex, old sex, moving in together sex*
- **rubbing** *cunts and clits together, cunts against thighs, against breasts,*

rubbing breasts against cunts, cunts against bums, tits against faces, hair over faces, over backs, over bellies, over cunts, hands against cunts, against arseholes

- **talking**
  talking sweet
  talking low
  talking dirty
  talking funny
  talking histories, futures
  talking fantasy
  talking rough
  talking love
  talking fears
  talking desire
  and much, much more

Some sex language, some names, add your own:

- **cunt** *vagina, pussy, slit, beaver, fanny*
- **clit** *clitoris, pearl, button, love spot*
- **arsehole** *anus, shit hole*
- **secretions** *wet, juices, cream, cum*
- **breasts** *boobs, tits*
- **rimming** *ass-licking*
- **fisting** *hand-fucking*
- **cunnilingus** *going down on, eating out, eating pussy, muff diver, pearl diver*
- **fucking** *screwing, making love, intercourse, bonking, rooting*
- **female ejaculation** *stimulating the G-spot makes some women spurt out a liquid – definitely not urine*

It's not just because we live in the age of AIDS that we suggest that it's a positive and important thing for lesbians to talk about sex. We live in a world in which sex is continuously present, implied, conveyed – and repressed, misunderstood, judged – and desired. In most countries and cultures, lesbianism has been both unimaginable (invisible and/or disgusting) and titillating, a part of public and private fantasies. We have tended to have few public places in which to develop distinctly lesbian subcultures and have too often been invisible to each other. Recognizing the titillation value of lesbianism in the straight world has made us fearful of developing an explicit and popular lesbian language of lust and sex. Who might listen to our words and stories besides ourselves?

That lesbianism has become a sexual possibility for many more women in a number of countries during the past twenty years or so has helped create different lesbian subcultures, particularly in urban areas. But the fear of speaking publicly about what happens sexually between women has remained a continuing force. We talk around the subject: we talk about sexuality; we talk about love; we talk about who we fancy, who turns us on. But the majority of us don't talk about what we do, what we want to do, or what we fantasize about doing with another woman. Why?

First, many lesbians seem to believe that there is already a recognized and acceptable recipe for lesbian sex. But when questioned more closely, it often becomes clear that no one really knows what this recipe is, or who decided it was good and nutritious in the first place. It seems to go something like this: kissing, stroking, stimulating the clit with fingers or tongue, perhaps a finger or two inserted into the cunt. This can be romantic, swooning stuff, or sweaty, rolling-in-the-hay hard stuff. It can be mutually accomplished or not, although ideally each lover should have her needs met. All this is fine, but what do we really know? Do most lesbians go down on each other? How many use rubbing? Do fewer practise penetration? How do we know? Maybe some don't who are really dying for it? And what about everything else that girls might like to get up to with each other? What about heavy fucking with fingers, a hand or a dildo? How many get that, give that, want that? What about dressing up, playing roles, arse fucking, sitting on your lover's face, slurping into 69, tying her up, getting yourself blindfolded, and on and on and on? And what if you don't get sex? Don't want sex?

We're scared of talking. Scared we're going to be *wrong*, scared we're going to be judged.

Part of the trouble is that lesbians have had a problem talking openly in our community about sex, both between women and whether or not we partner with men. This means that it's very controversial for a lesbian to talk about whether or not she uses sex toys, she fucks men, or whether or not she rims or is rimmed by her girlfriend. When we start to talk about safer sex, what sex acts are we worried about – oral sex, blood?
Amber Hollibaugh

We live in a society which maintains that it celebrates individual choice and development. Yet really we seem to want all the individuals who make up society to behave according to certain rules. Within the lesbian communities in Britain and in the US, divisive, bitter, accusatory sexual politics ruled the roost during the 80s. Certain kinds of sexual practice were considered bad, not really lesbian, dangerous to women. Generally these were thought to be SM practices, whatever that means, but they also often included butch/femme behaviour. The legacy of those days is still with us. Lesbians' historical reticence and nervousness about talking about sex has been exacerbated by the bitter debates within lesbian sexual politics. Who wanted to risk being denounced, excommunicated from the lesbian club, labelled a terrible person because she talked openly or listened generously to a range of lesbian experiences?

But it isn't always about being judged for doing the supposedly 'wild' things. We're also scared of being judged by SM or pro-sex dykes who say or imply that if you aren't (at least) getting yourself strapped up and fucked with a dildo, then you're boring, caught up in your own fears and repressions. Where does the fear of being judged, caught out, embarrassed, thought silly, come from?

The strange thing in the community I'm part of is that on the one hand we talk a lot about sex, but on the other there are so many prescriptive notions around which are the result of years of politics about what sex is acceptable and what isn't. Anything we do, like, or desire that doesn't fit in with the supposed norms of whatever lesbian community you come from, is censored in any debate. And then there's still the business of being a woman and being worried you're doing something unacceptable. In order to explore issues which may be taboo and difficult, we have to stop being judgmental and start to be honest.
Da Choong

The ease with which we can talk about sex is informed by our personal histories and can be culturally specific, too.

For a lot of Asian women, sex is a taboo subject in our families and culture and we never talk about it. I have found it difficult to talk about sex; then to talk about safer sex is another issue altogether. Madhu

Perhaps some of our fear comes from the difficulty of being truthful about something so often private and elusive, and so hard to convey in words. Sex is physical and present, but it is also bound up with desire, which is cerebral, perverse, subconscious and unpredictable. Does acknowledging that you really want to be fucked up the arse, held and rocked like a baby, or talk dirty to your partner(s) convey to others where desires come from, or what place they hold in your emotions? What feels intensely sexual in the dim light can sound ridiculous and banal in a non-sexual talk about sex. We have to make it clear that we won't judge ourselves or others, that no matter how ridiculous it feels, it isn't going to hurt to say it, that someone else has felt it too.

What HIV and AIDS have made clear for lesbians (and for all sexual human beings) is that we can't afford to allow the *shoulds* and *shouldn'ts* of sexual correctness, or received wisdom, to stunt our discussions. We don't have the leisure, the time, the space, to wait, to put off until tomorrow: we have to break through whatever it is that keeps us prisoners of our own fear. Once permission is given, once the floodgates are open, we can begin to perceive the beginnings of a collective exploration of lesbian cultures of sexuality. It is only then that we will be an active part of the ferment which is taking place, in large part due to the AIDS crisis, around sexuality.

We want to be able to celebrate the diversity of lesbian sex with more knowledge of what that diversity means in practice. In itself this isn't enough, but it is essential in order to resist any fundamentalist attempts to restrict sexual acts to what a person, group or society thinks is correct or incorrect.

Safer sex: to suck or not to suck?

I used to practise safer sex but I stopped because of all the conflicting information and because I hate dental dams which I find really uncomfortable. But that doesn't mean I don't talk about it with whoever I'm with. It's being able to talk and negotiate your fears around it that's important. Madhu

We believe that safer sex is something lesbians should know about, and should know how to practise if appropriate, for the following reasons:

- Safer-sex techniques are possible ways of protecting lesbian sexual health from STDs in general, including herpes, chlamydia, warts, crabs, hepatitis, gardenerella and other vaginal infections. The possibility of using safer-sex techniques selectively in relation to your own or a lover's STD is a health- and sex-positive move. Lesbians having one-off sexual encounters, even if not worried about HIV, might think about other, more easily picked-up or passed-on, STDs. Repeated bouts of vaginal infections are not insignificant annoyances, and herpes is for life.

  Lesbians do not take their sexual health seriously enough. Lesbians often believe that they 'don't pass on nasty things to each other'. Sorry girls, if you're lucky, fine, but lots of lesbians pass things on and back and forth. Others are nervous of going to a doctor or clinic because they fear anti-lesbianism, or a lack of understanding about lesbian sex. *My doctor told me I didn't need a cervical smear because lesbians didn't get cervical cancer. Even though that's a myth, I had to tell her that quite a few of us were heterosexual before.*

The success of the recently founded Sandra Bernhard Clinic for lesbian health in London shows the need for facilities lesbians can use, and medical staff who understand their needs.

We set up the Sandra Bernhard Clinic in April 1992 because we felt that there was very little information about lesbians and sexually transmitted diseases. We were concerned that lesbians were not being given access to services they needed. Many lesbians have questions about their sexual practices and concerns about whether they could transmit certain sexual

diseases to their partners. We wanted to create a safe environment for lesbians to be open, in which the onus isn't on them to come out to potentially hostile doctors. We also wanted to offer HIV testing and a safe space to discuss safer sex and give women the latest research and information. The clinic is fully booked for months in advance and is very popular. Sandy Nelson

- For the lesbian who is already positive, safer sex can be a protection from STDs which might have more serious consequences in a positive body, particularly hepatitis B and C, thrush and herpes. Taking this into account is responsible and smart. Women who assume they are not positive could think about the possibility of having a sexual relationship or encounter with a positive woman not only in terms of the possibilities (or fears) of lesbian transmission, but also in terms of *what danger could I be to this wonderful woman I fancy and how can I be safer for her?*

There are lots of STDs that are easy to pass on through lesbian sex and are much more likely to be transmitted through the kind of sex lesbians have than HIV is. But most lesbians don't know anything about them. There is also evidence emerging that STDs have quite a lot to do with transmission – as possible co-factors. And more lesbians have STDs than is popularly believed. It would be useful if the debate about HIV/AIDS was a platform for lesbians to start taking their sexual health more seriously. I think that's important. Da Choong

- Safer sex is a skill we can all know about and then choose to use or not as the situation demands. Identities can be multiple and changing. The woman who fucks only women today may be the one who falls for a man tomorrow. Safer sex in these circumstances takes on a very different meaning and priority. Having a lesbian identity does not protect you from HIV in other circumstances. Lesbianism in itself is not a condom!

- Safer sex can be a way of exploring different sexual practices. Latex gloves, with a coat of non-oil-based lubricant on the fingers, might enable some shit-scared lesbians to try a bit of anal stimulation (remembering that you never force fingers or objects into an unrelaxed anus). Using dental dams to cover up the arsehole and then licking (rimming) it could drive your sweetie wild, take away either partner's nervousness of shit, and protect from hepatitis (which is much more easily transmitted than HIV). Put a bit of non-oil-based lubricant on the arsehole before covering it with the latex – it makes it more pleasurable for the licked one. Doing the same with a dam for licking cunts and clits could free up women who are scared off by vaginal juices and smells, including menstrual ones. For further information on safer-sex accessories, see page 51.

• Playing with safer-sex bits and bobs could be the first truly hysterically funny sexual encounter you have with a partner. The slurp and slush of a too-big latex glove while fucking your girlfriend's cunt is quite an experience. (Properly fitting latex gloves are the most easily eroticized safer-sex accessory – some lesbians say that just hearing the snap of the glove going on gets them hot.)

• Talking about the ways you might want to use safer-sex techniques can turn into a session of sexual openness and fantasy. And don't forget that sex toys are the easiest safer-sex fun around. A dildo or vibrator only needs a change of condom between shares in order to protect from thrush, herpes and warts. If condoms aren't around, be sure to wash it well in hot water with soap, and rinse off.

• Uncertainty is part of life, particularly as millions of us live it today. Many old certainties have gone or transmuted, new ones are still around the corner. Perhaps for one woman it's more important to use clean needles when shooting up than to worry about the less likely possibility of becoming positive through lesbian sex. Perhaps someone else will decide that if there is a one-in-a-million chance of transmission, that's enough to cause worry, and so will want to practise safer sex and be able to stop worrying. If you believe (or fear) there is a minute possibility of transmission, then you might decide to evaluate it as you do other risky activities: driving in cars, walking alone at night, smoking.

• Finally, safer sex is part of a big and varied sexual conversation of the 80s and 90s, sometimes troubled and horrifying, sometimes new and exciting. That doesn't mean that all lesbians must practise it in order to be part of a new lesbian political correctness. But it does mean that everyone should know the rudiments of safer sex in order to be informed and to able to make more than theoretical choices.

It is always instructive to ask yourself if you would go down on a woman (or man) who told you they were positive, especially if you assume you're negative. It might make you stop and think, no matter what your beliefs about woman-to-woman transmission. Even if your initial response is no, that doesn't mean you would continue to feel that way. Thinking, talking, getting information, can change feelings of fear. And if you are positive yourself, you may not want anyone to go down on you without using latex, for fear of picking up a secondary infection.

Who knows when a woman you want to make love with will ask you to use safer-sex techniques? Or when knowledge and information about them would make it easier for you to start a seduction? Who knows when or where you might be called upon to educate someone: a friend's teenager, your own kids, their friends, your brother or sister, your friends, your mother, a colleague? We may not choose to deliver safer-sex speeches at every opportunity, but we may find ourselves in situations where we are the only ones who will, or can, and we should be able to do it.

Safer sex: the basics

Where HIV is present

HIV is transmitted primarily through blood and semen. In theory, HIV can be found in all bodily fluids; however, its concentration in different bodily fluids varies hugely. The lower the concentration, the lower the likelihood of transmission of the virus.

Blood and semen have the highest concentrations; vaginal juices and pre-cum (what leaks from the penis before ejaculation) lower concentrations. The presence of a vaginal infection seems to increase the concentration of HIV in a positive woman's vagina. The concentration in tears, saliva and probably piss is so low as to present no chance of transmission at all. The bodily fluid in shit probably has a very low level of HIV, so shit in itself is probably not a dangerous route of HIV transmission (although it can carry other infectious amoebas and viruses). If shit contains infected blood, obviously that blood will contain higher levels of HIV. However, the amount of blood in shit, unless a person is haemorrhaging, is very small, and by the time it is ready to come out, it may be old, dried blood in which the HIV is no longer active.

Routes of transmission

HIV is passed on when blood, semen, or less often vaginal fluids or pre-cum from a positive person directly enters another person's bloodstream, either through actively open wounds or mucose membranes (the mucose-secreting linings of various cavities in the body such as the nose, anus and vagina). The mucose membrane of the anus is more delicate than that of the vagina, so anal fucking is more likely to create open cuts in the anus through which the virus can enter the bloodstream.

The main routes of HIV transmission are through unsafe sex with a positive person; through sharing unclean needles to inject drugs; through the use of unclean needles for injections in hospitals and clinics in countries where there is not enough money for disposable needles (injecting drugs with clean needles is safe in relation to HIV); through infected blood, blood products, and donated organs that contain HIV (since 1985 all these have been tested for HIV before use in the UK and US); possibly through transfer from mother to baby during pregnancy. None of these activities is guaranteed to pass the virus on. As one positive woman said:

You never know if it's going to be the third time, the thirty-ninth time, or the first time you have unsafe sex with a positive person that transmission of the virus happens. It's always a Russian roulette.

Sexual transmission most often occurs through infected semen being ejaculated into the vagina or anus. That's why the major safer-sex message continues to be aimed at preventing men from depositing infected semen into vaginas and anuses. Condoms are the main way of keeping semen out of these places. Gay men who have used these for anal sex have been successful in stopping transmission.

A positive woman can transmit HIV to men through vaginal fucking, although it appears less likely to happen this way round than from man to woman. Again, condoms protect. Positive people of either sex will want to protect themselves from getting new infections of HIV which could compromise their health further.

Self-insemination

Lesbians have been concerned about whether or not there is a risk of HIV transmission to either themselves or their foetus if they are using donated sperm from a positive man for self-insemination. This is another grey area in which the risks are still unknown. Anyone wishing to use donated sperm for self-insemination will want to use healthy sperm and therefore to avoid HIV-positive sperm. Guidelines include having the donor – gay, straight or bisexual – test for HIV antibodies twice, six months apart, and for him to agree to practise only safer sex between tests and for the duration of the donation. The only information about transmission from donated sperm relates to an Australian case reported in 1985, in which four heterosexual women attending an infertility clinic seroconverted after being inseminated with the semen of a donor later found to be positive. We have never seen any other cases discussed or reported.

Inseminating with 'fresh' semen is more likely to result in pregnancy than the frozen stuff which has been tested twice for HIV that all clinics now use. And many lesbians fear rejection or judgment at fertility clinics, and therefore prefer self-insemination. Most gay donors will expect to be asked for HIV test results; straight men may well not have given an HIV test a thought. In the end, you have to trust your donor and feel confident he will tell you the truth about his status and sexual practice.

Ultimately it comes down to trust. However many tests he does it means nothing if you don't trust he's always going to practise safer sex in between. Da Choong

Are we positive?

Not everyone who is HIV positive knows, or even suspects it. Unfortunately, there are men (and women) who do suspect or know their positive status and who continue to have unsafe sex. It therefore makes sense for heterosexuals, bisexuals and gay men to know about and practise safer sex if there is any reason at all to doubt their own or their partner's status, whether in a long-term relationship or not.

Even committed couples find it difficult to be 100 per cent truthful about their sexual histories, past and present. How many times have we heard ourselves or other women say, *It came as a complete and utter shock to me. I honestly believed we were faithful to each other and there were no signs that he/she was sleeping with anyone else?* On the other hand, blanket rules about *everyone* needing to practise safer sex don't help the credibility of safer-sex education. For some couples, it is fair enough to make the decision that they truly are monogamous and have been for long enough or are sure enough of their status not to worry about sexual transmission of the virus. Of course they have to trust that if the situation changes, they will tell one another and so can change the rules.

Assessing the risks

These are the basics of safer sex. Everything else has to be evaluated by individuals or communities in the light of new information, acceptability of risk, or even, in the absence of clear guidelines, a 'better safe than sorry' outlook.

No one contests that HIV exists in vaginal secretions at lower levels of concentration than in blood or semen. But does it exist in high enough concentrations to be transmitted during oral sex? Very little safer-sex advice for heterosexuals contains negative information about mouth-to-vagina oral sex. There is evidence which suggests that saliva has a neutralizing effect on the virus, rendering it harmless, especially when it is present in a low concentration, as in vaginal juices. In addition, it is known that HIV is destroyed by stomach juices, so even gay men are now being advised by many gay HIV health workers and health activists that oral sex is not dangerous.

HIV can be transmitted from women to men during vaginal fucking, probably through cuts in the tender skin of the unprotected penis. Transmission from the vagina would be much less likely to happen through finger-fucking, even if there were tiny sores on the fingers. And it would be even more difficult for a positive person's fingers, even chewed ones, to transmit HIV to a partner's cunt. *RELAX!* It's good to remember that in order to get in, the virus has to come into contact with actively open cuts and sores. It has to go right into the bloodstream. In most circumstances this is a very weak virus – it doesn't survive well outside certain conditions in the human body. As has been said a million times, you don't get it from toilet seats, from drinking glasses, from coughs or sneezes, or from kissing. And it seems clearer and clearer that all sex is not equally risky.

Things have changed a lot in the last year or two. When I first joined Terence Higgins Trust the talk was all about dental dams. Providing dental dams was a way of discussing the issue with lesbians and a way for them to start thinking about it seriously. Dental dams have never

been tested as an HIV barrier, aren't easily available and are not easy to use. But we were providing condoms for men, so we had to provide something for lesbians to use. That was the thinking at the time, although there are still lots of women who believe it. But it is inconsistent. Dental dams have never been pushed for heterosexuals: they are always for lesbians. So I do think it was a way of introducing the subject to the lesbian community. Da Choong

Lists of high-, middle- and low-risk sexual behaviours can become obsessive, frightening and confusing. In the past, we wondered why fisting (insertion of the whole hand in the arse or vagina) was listed as high risk in many safer-sex do's and don'ts. Was the risk to the fisting person or to the fisted person? If the fisting person was wearing a latex glove, was that safe? Given that semen was the major problem and hands don't (call us naïve) produce it directly, why were fisting hands up in the list along with fucking with unprotected penises? If the fisted person was in danger, what from? Blood from the fister? Surely it was very unlikely either that someone would put a profusely bleeding hand into a cunt or an arsehole or that vaginal juices or anal matter would pose much risk to a hand?

It seems that the logic of the advice (largely unstated) was that fisting anally or vaginally could cause cuts or abrasions – especially in the arse. If the fisted (and injured) person was then fucked with an unprotected penis, there was a higher chance of transmission of HIV. Why wasn't this stated clearly? Along with commentators like Pat Califia, we can only surmise that safer-sex guidelines, especially older ones, incorporated the writers' prejudices and fears about sex. Fisting is not considered proper or acceptable gay sexual behaviour by some gay men and lesbians. The same story could be told about SM sexual practices, which often found their way into the riskiest lists when in fact most should have been included in the safest list, whatever the list-makers thought of SM.

All this illustrates how important it is to separate off acknowledgment and acceptance of consensual sexual practices from personal endorsement of what's exciting and not exciting in sex. *Whatever anyone thinks of a particular sexual activity should not have anything to do with how it is analysed in relation to safer sex.*

As we open up discussions of lesbian sex, less known, more 'daring' sexual acts may appear as better, more exciting, and the women who do them may present themselves or be seen by others as being freer and more open. We've said it before and we'll say it again. Just because someone fists a woman, wearing leather, upside down, with nipple clamps on, does not mean she is any more exciting, interesting, witty, funny, sexually skilled or successful than anyone else. Someone who promotes vanilla sex is not necessarily a better lesbian feminist. 'Daring' sex can be kissing. Skilled, successful, hot sex can be cunnilingus. Exciting people can prefer vanilla. Interesting people can like SM. Witty women can adore massage. Funny dykes can desire a dildo. Just as being a lesbian doesn't automatically mean a woman is politically progressive or radical, so certain forms of lesbian sex do not automatically imply anything else about the women who practise them.

Demystifying our sex lives by talking about what we do, and seeing that communication as part of safer sex in its widest sense, can only help create a collective idea of the meaning of HIV in lesbian lives.

The agnostic position

We know that HIV and AIDS have not struck different lesbian communities with the same ferocity as they have gay mens'. We know that there have not been large numbers of women infected through lesbian sex before that route was considered a possible route of transmission. Thankfully, we are not in the position of gay men, who have to make safer sex part of their sexual lives.

But this does not mean that we don't worry about the breadth of our choices. Even if we don't believe that woman-to-woman transmission is a risk worth all of us practising safer sex for, we may still end up dreaming dreadful dreams of vaginal juices, saliva, shit, tears and menstrual blood teaming with HIV. Or we may believe that there are cases of lesbian sexual transmission, and that unless we are sure of our own and our partners' status, safer sex is an essential safeguard. Or that while, as lesbians or in our own particular relationship(s), we don't need actively to engage in safer sex, we do see it as important to put our energies into HIV/AIDS work and activism, into pushing for more research on women and HIV, as well as for more resources for gay men and other affected communities.

For us, the agnostic position feels the safest. It leaves the way open for those lesbians who are worried, and can't resolve that worry, to use safer sex. But it also indicates how pressing it is for us to build a framework in which to place our worries, our information, our politics, our uncertainties, and our knowledge. Not all decisions are rational or make total sense, especially those around sex! Deciding to practise safer sex with another woman in specific circumstances may not always be rational, but may make that sexual encounter a freer, more exciting, more caring experience. Conversely, deciding not to practise safer sex with another woman in specific circumstances may be a rational risk assessment of the danger of HIV transmission, but leaves herpes or hepatitis out of the equation. Deciding that making love with your sweetie with no reference to safer sex is not a risk in relation to HIV seems a possible responsible choice for lesbians as well. In celebration of our perversity, we should be revelling in the wealth and breadth of the sexual choices we can make in the time of AIDS and joining with others to end the epidemic, to continue to care for those affected by it, and to be a strong, radical force in sexual politics.

Make no mistake. We need to be open and accepting of our sexual lives and desires in all their diversity and mystery in order to be strong in our sexual politics. Even if lesbians are not in danger of transmitting HIV through woman-to-woman sex, it does not mean that we are mere onlookers in the AIDS crisis, involving ourselves as 'ladies with lamps'.

Worldwide, sexual politics is in flux. HIV and AIDS have become the vehicle for wider struggles over sexual freedom, homosexuality, women's liberation, family values, and sexual pleasure, diversity and difference. We are a part of this and without doubt the outcomes of these various debates and struggles will have profound and far-reaching effects on our lives.

Lesbians and a politics of HIV

We want to talk about what HIV and AIDS means for us as lesbians and queers in a hostile world.

- We want to begin to build a flexible framework of ideas that will help lesbians (and others) to make sense of their uncertainty and confusion in relation to HIV and AIDS.

- We want to talk openly about lesbian sexual practices, because until that happens, collectively and individually, we can't be confident about where we fit into any AIDS discourse. We are pro-sex, but non-judgmentally critical women, and we believe that lesbians need to open up, to stop being so fearful of being wrong – about what they do in bed, what they want to do there, or even what they don't want to do in bed or anywhere else.

- We want to point out where we think logic breaks down in sexual-health messages to lesbians, particularly those to do with safer sex.

- But we are not interested in either/or messages – either we're at risk from unsafe lesbian sex or we're not, full stop. We believe that the AIDS crisis affects everyone, but with different intensities. A vital and radical challenge to AIDS would weave together these differences, while fully acknowledging and validating the pain, anger and needs of gay men in the face of homophobia and indifference, and the undeniable continuing impact AIDS has on them.

- This challenge would consider the devastation of people in Asia and Africa, and the impact of the virus on poor and/or black people in the US, both situations undeniably bound up with an ongoing history of racism and exploitation.

- It would recognize the different ways the epidemic is affecting a range of groups and would consign to the rubbish heap the notion that different groups asserting their need of AIDS resources take away from other groups. The idea that *gay men* are competing with *women*, are competing with *drug users*, are competing with *Africans*, are competing with *Asians* for resources fits very nicely into a divide-and-rule perspective.

- We can only meet the needs of specific groups if we admit *everyone* affected by HIV and AIDS to the arena. Supporting the differing needs of groups and communities need not take away from the groups most in need, or most disowned by society. It need not ignore or downplay the serious health crises women face besides HIV and AIDS – such as breast cancer. Rather, a united response could be a more effective means of exerting enough pressure on governments and agencies and people with money, power and resources to meet the needs of everyone affected by HIV.

- Our challenge would *develop* the different levels of response to HIV and AIDS that lesbians could have and would understand that most people do not live in hermetically sealed communities. The recognition that positive lesbians exist challenges old fixed notions of lesbian identity. These are lesbians who have mostly become positive through IV drug use or having sex with men. They should be supported and accepted in our lesbian cultures, our homes and our hearts.

Information and contacts

AIDS and HIV: some definitions

HIV (Human Immunodeficiency Virus)

HIV is a virus, but not an ordinary one. On the simplest level, when someone is infected with this virus, their body reacts by producing antibodies. That is what the standard HIV test reveals: antibodies to the HIV virus. A person with such antibodies is HIV positive. The time it takes for HIV antibodies to be produced by a body varies between six weeks and eighteen months, or even longer. This is called 'window' time.

However, the antibodies which the body produces are not able to get rid of HIV, and the virus remains in the person's body, probably for life. Some positive people will develop full-blown AIDS, others will not. There are now predictions that at least 50 per cent of positive people will *not* develop AIDS within ten years of living with the virus. Some will get ill and be diagnosed with AIDS a lot sooner. Why some people remain healthy and others don't is still not understood.

Many people who are HIV positive have no symptoms of illness; they feel well and have no health problems. Others may have illnesses from time to time, but remain essentially well and able to continue their lives as before. If someone positive becomes ill, it does not necessarily mean they have AIDS. Positive people who get ill can get better and remain healthy for years.

AIDS (Acquired Immuno Deficiency Syndrome)

AIDS is not a single disease or infection. People do not catch AIDS. AIDS stands for Acquired Immuno Deficiency Syndrome and is diagnosed at a point when the immune system has broken down to such an extent that the person is unable to resist relatively common, treatable infections. A positive person receives an AIDS diagnosis on the basis of developing one or more of a list of more than 120 opportunistic infections and cancers associated with being HIV positive. These include pneumonia, enteritis, meningitis, infections of the mucous membranes in the mouth or vagina, herpes, and a form of cancer called Kaposi's Sarcoma (KS). Although there is no cure for AIDS, treatments of certain diseases and conditions associated with AIDS are becoming more and more successful. People who have been diagnosed as having AIDS can recover from the illnesses which led to that diagnosis and remain well for a long time.

There is more and more evidence that AIDS can manifest itself differently in women than in men. Since most medical investigation has concentrated on men, women and their doctors have not necessarily been aware of complaints common to women, which may indicate a positive status, or the worsening of a positive woman's health. Some of these include pelvic inflammatory disease (PID), problems with menstruation, vaginal thrush, abnormal Pap smears and cervical cancer, and vaginal warts. Women may want to take various preventive measures to enhance their health, including regular Pap smears, using natural therapies, and developing more body self-knowledge and the confidence to insist that the medical profession take women's health complaints seriously.

There is much that remains a mystery about HIV and AIDS. Some people are not convinced that HIV *is* the cause of AIDS and feel that their critiques are being brushed aside by the medical establishment. If HIV is the cause of AIDS, we still do not understand the role of co-factors such as other sexually transmitted diseases, other infections, poverty, malnutrition, or serious environmental pollution, which may create susceptibility to the virus, or a predisposition to the development of HIV-associated illnesses in a positive person. In this book we have used the HIV explanation of AIDS, although we do not believe that the full story is known. But whatever the ultimate explanation or understanding of HIV and AIDS, through observation and experience we do know that certain activities and practices are, in certain circumstances, risky ones for transmitting whatever it is that may cause people's immune systems to crumble in such a destructive way.

HIV and AIDS are not the same thing. It may seem like nit-picking to insist on specific ways of referring to HIV and AIDS, but the way these words are used reverberates on real men and women living with HIV and AIDS.

Safer-sex accessories

Dental dams/oral shields

A 150mm (6 inch) square of pure latex, the dental dam/oral shield is used as a barrier for oral sex (vaginal or anal). It is stretched across the vulva (including the clitoris, vagina and labia) for cunnilingus or the anus for rimming, and held in place with the fingers. A water-based lubricant smeared on the side of the shield against the vulva increases sensation and helps to keep the dam in place.

Some guidelines suggest a dental dam should be used only once, then discarded. Most sources, however, describe ways of cleaning it safely for re-use. Washing it in a 10 per cent bleach solution is often recommended, but can cause skin irritation, so washing in a warm solution of mild detergent followed by a cold rinse may be preferred. Dry flat on a clean towel or tissue. Check for holes by holding up against the light. Colour codes for each partner can help identify which one is whose. Marking one side avoids confusion over which side should be in contact with the mouth.

Dental dams are available free from the Angel Project, Bernhard Clinic (see page 59 for details), and to women with HIV from Positively Women, Body Positive groups and HIV services (see pages 53 and 54). Details of retail outlets are given below.

Finger cots

Often found in first-aid kits, finger cots can be used to encase a digit for single finger-fucking. They can be bought at most medical suppliers and chemists.

Latex/surgical gloves

Latex/surgical gloves cover the whole hand and can be used for fist- or multi-finger-fucking. Some users cut off the wrist area to create a dental dam/oral shield. They can be bought at most medical suppliers and chemists.

Condoms

Placing a new condom on a vibrator, dildo or any other object used for penetration before passing the object to a partner to use helps prevent the exchanging of body fluids and transmission of STDs. Washing sex toys thoroughly in hot water is suggested as an alternative when condoms are unavailable.

For those who find dental dams/oral shields too thick, difficult to acquire or costly, condoms provide a greater range of thickness, colour, texture and taste. To transform a condom into a dental dam/oral shield: cut off tip, slit lengthwise (sharp scissors minimize wayward tearing), unroll and stretch out into a flat piece of material. Unlubricated condoms are easier to cut up; if lubricated condoms are used, make sure the lubricated side is against the vulva as condom lube tastes pretty nasty.

Condoms can be acquired free from local Body Positive groups, HIV services, Brook Advisory Centres, Family Planning Centres, Needle Exchanges, Genito-Urinary (STD) and Well Woman Clinics. They can be purchased from supermarkets, garages, chemists, slot machines in toilets and by mail order.

Caring for latex

Remember to keep all latex safer-sex accessories away from strong heat and sunlight. Rinse any latex products treated with talc before first usage. Avoid oil-based lubricants such as Vaseline as these cause the rubber to deteriorate; water-based lubricants such as K-Y Jelly are ideal.

Retail suppliers

Collonnades Chemists Stocks dental dams/oral shields (six flavours or 'natural'), finger cots, latex/surgical gloves and flavoured condoms. Anyone daunted by the prospect of verbally requesting safer-sex accessories can be reassured that staff are described as broadminded and welcoming and that the products are available self-service or by mail order. Chris Spinos, who runs the chemist, has produced his own free leaflet on the history, usage and care of dental dams/oral shields. He has taken out a world patent on a new improved oral shield, which will be a larger square and as thin as a condom. It is on hold until he is aware of sufficient demand. 30 Porchester Road, London W2 6ES Tel: 071 727 5713

Condomania Large choice of condoms plus dental dams and latex/surgical gloves. The Balcony, The Corn Exchange, Call Lane, Leeds LS1 Tel: 0532 446532; Liverpool Palace, 6-10 Slater Street, Liverpool L1 Tel: 051 707 0189; 57 Rupert Street, London W1 Tel: 071 287 4540

Expectations Sex shop stocking a range of dental dams/oral shields, latex/surgical gloves and condoms. 75 Great Eastern Street, London EC2 3HU Tel: 071 739 0292

Health Co UK Ltd Supplies dental dams/oral shields, latex/surgical gloves and condoms. 196 Great Cambridge Road, Enfield, Middlesex EN1 1UN Tel: 081 366 4412

John Bell and Croyden Medical suppliers stocking a range of latex/surgical gloves and finger cots. 54 Wigmore Street, London WI Tel: 071 935 5555

SHH! Sex shop run by women for women. Safer-sex packs available at cost price (including dental dams, condoms, lubricants, etc). 22 Coronet Street, London N1 Tel: 071 613 5458

HIV/AIDS organizations

The Ace Project (AIDS Care Education Project) Provides local support, advice, training, education and information in the boroughs of Croydon, Sutton and Merton. The ACE Centre, Queens Hospital, Queen's Road, Croydon CR9 2PS Tel: 081 665 5000

ACT UP (AIDS Coalition To Unleash Power) Direct-action group campaigning to improve support for HIV/AIDS research and people with HIV/AIDS. c/o LLGC, 67-69 Cowcross Street, London EC1

AIDS Ahead Counselling and support services for deaf people. 144 London Road, Northwich, Cheshire CW9 5HH Tel: 0606 47047/0606 330472 (minicom) London: 081 348 9195/081 342 8791 (minicom)

The AIDS Education And Research Trust (AVERT) Medical research projects and education programmes. 11 Denne Parade, Horsham, West Sussex RH12 IJD Tel: 0403 210202

AKIRAH Care, counselling and information on issues of HIV/AIDS for African, Caribbean and Asian people. Riverhouse, Furnival Gardens, off Rutland Grove, London W6 Tel: 081 741 4772 (noon-5pm Thursday)

Black HIV/AIDS Network (BHAN) Counselling in Bengali, Gujerati, Hindi, Swahili, Urdu and on arrangement in Arabic, Amharic, Cantonese, Punjabi, Thai, Vietnamese and Chinese dialects. 111 Davenport Road, London W12 8PB Tel: 081 749 2828

Blackliners HIV/AIDS advice and support for African, Caribbean and Asian people. PO Box 1274, London SW8EX Tel: 071 738 5274

Body Positive Support, counselling and advice for people who are HIV positive. Keeps up-to-date information on nationwide services and of Body Positive groups. 5lb Philbeach Gardens, London SW5 9EB Tel: 071 835 1045 (office hours)/ 071 373 9124 (7pm-10pm daily)

Body Positive Women's Core Group National group that meets monthly at the Body Positive Centre to provide mutual support and to plan women's responses to HIV/AIDS. 51b Philbeach Gardens, London SW5 9EB Tel: 071 835 1045

The Food Chain London-wide organization providing hot meals to housebound people with HIV/AIDS and carers. Tel: 071 250 1391 (currently weekends only)

Hackney HIV Resource Centre Collection of books, magazines and leaflets on HIV/AIDS and related issues based at Stoke Newington Library, London. Details from the Health Promotion Unit on 081 533 0297

Haemophilia Society Information, advice and support for anyone who has haemophilia. Plus special representation of people infected with HIV through using Factor 8. 123 Westminster Bridge Road, London SE1 7HR Tel: 071 928 2020

Immune Development Trust Registered charity providing holistic treatments for people with HIV/AIDS, cancer and other immune-related illnesses. The Basement, Gatestone, Cromer Street, London WC1H 8EA Tel: 071 837 2151

Immunity's Legal Centre Free full-time specialist legal centre for anyone with legal problems connected to HIV/AIDS or related conditions. 206a Kilburn Lane, London W10 4BA Tel: 081 968 8909 (10am-5pm weekdays)

The Landmark Day centre for people with HIV/AIDS. Holds open women-only evenings each Wednesday. 47 Tulse Hill, London SW2 Tel: 081 671 7611 Referrals: 081 678 6687 Admin: 081 678 6686

London Lighthouse Centre for all people facing the challenge of AIDS. Counselling, drop-in facility, play group, creative-writing classes, residential care, training. Support groups include one for women with HIV/AIDS each Monday (7pm-9.30pm) and a mixed group on Tuesdays (starting at 7pm) for people who have just found out they are HIV positive. 111-117 Lancaster Road, London W11 1QT Tel: 071 792 1200

Lothian Health Board HIV/AIDS Team 11 Drumsheugh Gardens, Edinburgh E3 7QQ Tel: 031 225 1341 x2298

Mainliners Support groups and advice for people with HIV/AIDS who are, or have, been drug users. 205 Stockwell Road, London SW9 95L Tel: 071 737 3141

Meditation Group For people with HIV/AIDS at the London Buddhist Centre, 51 Roman Road, E2. Information on 081 981 0091

Mildmay Hospital Mission Convalescence, respite and terminal care provided by an independent Christian charity. Plus day care and 24-hour call-out home-care service, covering City and East London. Mother-and-baby rooms available. Hackney Road, London E2 7NA Tel: 071 729 2331 or 071 739 9351

Names Project British arm of the worldwide quilt memorial to individuals who have lost their lives to AIDS. 86 Constitution Street, Edinburgh EH6 6RP Tel: 031 555 3446 Quilt-making sessions at **London Lighthouse** (see above) each Thursday

National Aids Manual (NAM) Comprehensive and regularly updated UK directory of HIV/AIDS treatments and clinical trials. Unit 52, The Eurolink Centre, 49 Effra Road, London SW2 1BZ Tel: 071 737 1846

National AIDS Trust Co-ordinates and serves the voluntary sector. Women's Development Officer: Liz Dibb.14th Floor, Euston Tower, 286 Euston Road, London NW1 3DN Tel: 071 383 4246

The Naz Project HIV/AIDS service for the South Asian and Muslim communities. Palingswick House, 241 King Street, London W6 9LP Tel: 081 563 0191 (admin). See page 56 for times and numbers of five different language helpline services

Northern Lights Trust AIDS-mastery workshops which focus on visualization and other healing techniques. BM Breathe, London WC1N 3XX Tel: 0992 576649

Nurses Support Group Runs advice line for nursing staff needing information on and help with HIV/AIDS issues. Tel: 071 708 5605 (7pm-10pm Monday and Wednesday)

Positively Catholics For Catholics with HIV/AIDS. PO Box 646, London EP9 6QP Tel: 081 968 0807

Positively Irish Action On AIDS Support and information for Irish people affected by HIV/AIDS in the UK. St Margaret House, 21 Old Ford Road, London E2 9PL Tel: 081 983 0192 (admin) 081 983 4293 (referrals)

Positively Women Support and counselling services run by women for women who are HIV positive and for children directly affected by HIV. Many local support groups around London, including one for African women. Produces a range of leaflets on HIV issues for women and offers training to the voluntary and statutory sectors. Free dental dams to HIV-positive women. 5 Sebastian Street, London EC1V 0HE Tel: 071 490 5501 (admin) 071 490 5515 (client services)

Positive Options Nationwide Barnados scheme providing information, advice and support where one parent or both are HIV positive and want to make plans for the future care of their children. Also offers support to children and their families where a child is HIV positive. 354 Goswell Road, London EC1V 7LQ Tel: 071 278 5039

Positive Partners Self-help support for anyone affected by HIV/AIDS. The Annexe, Jan Rebane Centre, 12-14 Thornton Street, London SW9 0BL Tel: 071 738 7333 (**Positively Children** is also based here)

Positive Women Edinburgh c/o Scottish AIDS Monitor, 64 Broughton Street, Edinburgh EH11 3SA Tel: 031 555 4850

Positive Women Glasgow c/o Scottish AIDS Monitor, 22 Woodside Terrace, Glasgow G3 7XB Tel: 041 353 3133

Positive Youth Group for people living with HIV or AIDS who are twenty-six and under. Drop-in each Friday at the **Body Positive Centre**, 51b Philbeach Gardens, London SW5 9EB Tel: 071 373 7547

Scottish AIDS Monitor Offers a comprehensive range of care and prevention services and holds details of services for all areas of Scotland. PO Box 169, Edinburgh Tel: 031 555 4850

SHARE (Shakti HIV/AIDS Response) Support group for South Asian people with HIV/AIDS. c/o The Landmark, 47 Tulse Hill, London SW2 Tel: 081 678 6686

Solas HIV centre with a full range of services including complementary therapies. 2-4 Abbeymount, Edinburgh EH8 8EJ Tel: 031 661 0982

Strutton Housing Association Specialist housing association for people who are HIV positive. There is no waiting list and direct referrals are not accepted. 8 Strutton Ground, London SW1P 2HP Tel: 071 222 5921

Supported Accommodation Team Aids (SATA) Supportive housing for people with HIV/AIDS. 20 Albany Street, Edinburgh EH1 3QB Tel: 031 556 9140

Terrence Higgins Trust Practical support, help, counselling and advice for people with or people concerned about HIV/AIDS. Women counsellors, buddies and Helpline volunteers available on request. Up-to-date specialist library facilities and health-education facilities for women and lesbians. Helpline advice numbers on page 56. 52-54 Grays Inn Road, London WC1 8JU Tel: 071 831 0330

Threshold Housing Association General housing agency providing support and housing to people who are HIV positive. 467 Garratt Lane, London SW18 4SN Tel: 081 874 1680

The Women's Group Support group for women with HIV/AIDS in the north-west of England. PO Box 201, Manchester M60 IPU Tel: 061 839 4340

The UK Coalition For People Living With HIV/AIDS c/o London Lighthouse, 111-117 Lancaster Road, London W11 1QT Tel: 071 792 1200

Helplines

AIDS Helpline Northern Ireland 0232 326117

Afro-Caribbean Helpline Service Black advisers offering specialized support on any issue related to HIV/AIDS. All calls are free from anywhere in the UK. 0800 567123 (6pm-10pm Friday)

Bisexual Phonelines 081 569 7500 (7.30pm-9.30pm Tuesday and Wednesday) 031 557 3620 (7.30pm-9.30pm Thursday)

Black Lesbian and Gay Helpline 071 837 5364 (7pm-10pm Thursday)

Blackliners Helpline 071 738 5274 (1pm-4pm Tuesday-Friday)

Body Positive Helpline 071 373 9124 (7pm-10pm daily)

Edinburgh Lesbian Line 031 557 0751 (7.30pm-10pm daily)

Gay and Lesbian Legal Advice 071 253 2043 (7pm-10pm Monday-Friday)

Glasgow Lesbian Line 041 552 5768 (7pm-10pm Wednesday)

Gofal SDIC Gogledd Cymru (AIDS Care North Wales) 0492 860569

Jewish Lesbian and Gay Helpline 071 706 3132 (7pm-10pm Monday-Thursday)

London Bisexual Group 081 568 1072

London Friend Helpline 071 837 3337 (7.30pm-10pm daily)

London Friend Women's Helpline 071 873 2782 (7.30pm-10pm Tuesday-Thursday)

London Lesbian and Gay Switchboard 071 837 7324 (24 hours). Staffed by lesbian and gay volunteers who are trained to answer enquiries about HIV/AIDS and safer sex. Request to speak to a lesbian if preferred. Minicom facility available

London Lesbian Line 071 251 6911 (7pm-10pm weekdays. Monday and Friday 2pm start)

Manchester Lesbian and Gay Switchboard 061 274 3999

Narcotics Anonymous 071 351 6794

National AIDS Helpline All calls are free from anywhere in the UK. 0800 567123 (24 hours) 0800 521361 (minicom 10am-10pm daily). Bengali, Gujerati, Hindi, Punjabi and Urdu: 0800 282445 (6pm-10pm Wednesday); Cantonese 0800 282446 (6pm-10pm Tuesday); Arabic 0800 282447 (6pm-10pm Wednesday). Request to speak to a woman if preferred

The Naz HIV/AIDS Helplines
Turkish/English 081 563 0205 (6.30pm-10.30pm Monday); Punjabi/English 081 563 0205 (6.30pm-10.30pm Tuesday); Hindi/English 081 563 0208 (6.30pm-10.30pm Tuesday); Urdu/English 081 563 0205 (6.30pm-10.30pm Wednesday); Gujerati/English 081 563 0208 (6.30pm-10.30pm Wednesday)

PACE (Project for Advice, Counselling and Education) 071 251 2689

Piccadilly Advice Centre 071 434 3773 Information bank on London services

Positively Women 071 490 2327 (noon-2pm weekdays)

Rape Crisis Centre 071 837 1600

Refugee Council Helpline 071 582 6922 (2pm-5pm weekdays)

Release Emergency drug-related legal problems 071 603 8564

Shakti Women 081 802 8981

Strathclyde Gay Switchboard 041 221 8372 (7pm-10pm daily)

Terrence Higgins Trust 071 242 1010 (general 3pm-10pm daily); 071 405 2381 (legal line 7pm-10pm Wednesday); 0800 212529 (prisoners link 3pm-6pm Tuesday and Thursday)

Information for ex- and current drug users

Women are at risk of HIV infection when they share needles, syringes and other equipment used to inject drugs. Small amounts of blood can remain in equipment and then be injected into the bloodstream of the next user, transmitting any infection. Needle-exchange services can supply new needles and **SCODA** (details below) holds lists of services nationally. Always dispose of used works safely or through a syringe exchange. Where it is impossible to obtain new equipment: separate the needle, barrel and plunger and clean first in cold water (prevents the blood from thickening), then in a strong solution of washing-up liquid and clean hot tap water. Flush the needle and syringe out thoroughly several times. Wash spoons, mixing bowls or any other equipment in the same way.

Angel Project Advice and information for people with drug-related problems. Syringe exchange, free dental dams and condoms. Women-only sessions. 38-44 Liverpool Road, London N1 0PU Tel: 071 226 3113

Birmingham Drugs Line Dale House, New Meeting Street, Birmingham B4 7SX Tel: 021 632 6363

Blenheim Project Confidential support for lesbians who have recently stopped using substances (2pm-4pm Wednesday). 7 Thornton Close, London W10 Tel: 081 960 5599

Bridge Project 154 Mill Road, Cambridge CBl 3LP Tel: 0223 214614

Bristol Drugs Project 18 Guinea Street, Redcliffe, Bristol BSl 6SX

Caravan Needle Exchange Clean equipment offered. South Wharf Road, London W2 Tel: 071 725 1418

CHAOS (Community Health and Drugs Service) HIV testing and information, general health information and care, referrals, counselling on drugs, female doctor and nurse available. National Temperance Hospital, Hampstead Road, London NW1 Tel: 071 383 4888 (9am-5pm Monday-Thursday; 9am-2pm Friday)

Cleveland Street Needle Exchange 60a Cleveland Street, London W1 Tel: 071 631 1750

D.A.W.N. (Drugs, Alcohol, Women, Nationally) Advice and information for women experiencing drug/alcohol problems. Omnibus Workspace, 39-41 North Road, London N7 9DP Tel: 071 700 4653

Dunain House Addiction Unit Craig Dunain Hospital, Inverness, Scotland IV3 Tel: 0463 234101 x2218

Exeter Drugs Project The 59 Centre, 59 Magdalen Street, Exeter EX2 4HY Tel: 0392 410292

Liverpool Syringe Exchange Merseyside Regional AIDS Prevention, Maryland Centre, 8 Maryland Street, Liverpool L1 9BX Tel: 051 709 2231

Mainliners Support groups and advice for people with HIV/AIDS who are or have been drug users. 205 Stockwell Road, London SW9 9SL Tel: 071 737 3141

Narcotics Anonymous Lesbian and gay group for any type of drug problem. Meets weekly (7.30pm Tuesday) St Peter's Church Hall, 59a Portobello Road, London W11 Tel: 071 351 6794

Needle Exchange Free needles, syringes, swabs, sterile water, condoms and lubricants, referrals to rehabilitation and detoxification programmes, nurse available for healthcare, GP sessions, support and advice. Contact through

National Aids Helpline Tel: 0800 567123 (24 hours)

North East Council For Addictions/Women and Alcohol 1 Mosley Street, Newcastle-upon-Tyne Tel: 091 232 7878 (counselling); 091 232 0797 (information)

Release For drug-related legal problems. 169 Commercial Road, London E1 Tel: 071 377 5905 (071 603 8564 for emergencies)

SCODA (Standing Conference On Drug Abuse) The HIV Information Officer holds national lists of needle-exchange services. 1-4 Hatton Place, London EC1N 8ND Tel: 071 430 2341

Tim Cyffuriau Cymunedol Community Drug Team Community Drug Clinic, 46 Cowbridge Road East, Canton, Cardiff CFl 9DU Tel: 0222 395877/8

Women and AIDS Drug Dependents Anonymous Drug Dependents Anonymous, 1 Newcastle Chambers, Off Angel Row, Nottingham NGl 3HQ Tel: 0602 4122888

Information for sex workers

Centenary Project Support and non-judgmental counselling for women working in prostitution. HIV counselling and testing also offered. 37 Henderson House, Leith, Edinburgh Tel: 031 553 2490

CLASH (Central London Action On Street Health) Counselling, medical services and advice for young people. 15 Bateman Buildings, Soho Hospital, Soho Square, London W1V 5TW Tel: 071 734 1794

Maryland Centre Support, information and healthcare for women who work on the streets. 8 Maryland Street, Liverpool L1 9BX Tel: 051 709 2231

Praed Street Project Research project which also offers confidential STD checks and general women's health service for sex workers. Drop-in facility on Wednesday and Thursday (2pm-6pm). c/o Jefferies Wing , St Mary's Hospital, London W2 1NY Tel: 071 725 1549 (9am-5pm weekdays)

SAFE: Prostitute Research/Outreach Project Support, information and advice for women working in the sex industry. South Birmingham Health Authority, Vincent Drive, Edgbaston, Birmingham B15 2TZ Tel: 021 627 2058;
Well Woman clinic: 021 359 0653; Drop-in centre: 213 Mary Street, Balsall Heath, Birmingham B2 Tel: 021 443 4040

Scottish Prostitutes Education Project (SCOT-PEP) Support, information and advice for people who work in the sex industry. 21a Torphichen Street, Edinburgh EH8 8HX Tel: 031 229 8269

Sheffield AIDS Education Project Drop-in, advice, information and support for women who work in the sex industry. 37 Stone Grove, Sheffield S10 2SW Tel: 0742 754038

Lesbian/women's health

The Bernhard Clinic NHS service staffed by women specifically geared towards the needs of all women who have sex with women. Offers HIV testing, safer-sex information, free dental dams, health advice, counselling, breast screenings, cervical smears, screening for STDs and referrals. Dept of G.U. Medicine, Charing Cross Hospital, Fulham Palace Road, London W6. Appointments by phone for each Wednesday. Tel: 081 846 1576/7

British Pregnancy Advisory Service 7 Belgrave Road, London SW1
Tel: 071 222 0985

Campaign To Access To Donor Insemination Campaigning group to ensure equal access to donor insemination. c/o 52-52 Featherstone Street, London EC1

Homoeopathic Clinic For lesbians at the LLGC, 67-69 Cowcross Street, London ECI Bookings: 071 254 8494

Margaret Pike Centre Gynaecology centre which also does research. Free condoms, morning-after pill, pregnancy testing and advice. 15 Bateman Buildings, Soho Square, London W1 Tel: 071 734 9351

Rape Crisis Centre Confidential service of information, support and advice with details of UK local groups. PO Box 69, London WC1X 9NJ Tel: 071 837 1600

Women's Health (formerly Women's Health & Reproductive Rights Information Centre) A library of information on women's health issues including HIV/AIDS. Provides lists of clinics offering donor insemination. 52-54 Featherstone Street, London EC1Y 8RT Tel: 071 251 6580

Women's Therapy Centre Advice and information on psychotherapy and mental health or related issues by women for women, plus individual and group therapy and workshops. Runs courses specifically for lesbians. 6 Manor Gardens, London N7 Tel: 071 263 6200

Bibliography and filmography

Further reading

ACT UP/New York Women and AIDS Book Group, *Women, AIDS & Activism,* South End Press, Boston, 1990. Comprehensive work about women in the AIDS epidemic compiled by lesbian activists in ACT UP

Boffin, Tessa & Gupta, Sunil, *Ecstatic Antibodies: Resisting the AIDS mythology,* Rivers Oram Press, London, 1991

Bright, Susie, *Susie Sexpert's World of Lesbian Sex* Cleis Press, San Francisco-Pittsburgh, 1990. Chapters on the use of dental dams and safer-sex techniques for anal sex and fisting

Bright, Susie, *Virtual Reality,* Cleis Press, San Francisco-Pittsburgh, 1992. More wit and wisdom on safer sex for lesbians

Califia, Pat, *The Advocate Adviser,* Alyson Publications, Boston, 1991

Califia, Pat, *The Lesbian S/M Safety Manual: Basic health and safety for woman-to-woman,* S/M Lace Publications, Denver,1988. Safer sex from top to bottom

Califia, Pat, *Sapphistry,* Naiad Press, Tallahassee,1988. Includes the chapter: 'A Note On Lesbians and AIDS'

Carlomusto, Jean, 'Deep Inside Safer Sex Videos' in *On Our Backs,* January/February 1990 (US). Jean Carlomusto discusses her safer-sex porn video, *Current Flow*

Chu, S. et al, 'Epidemiology of reported cases of AIDS in lesbians United States 1980-89' in *American Journal of Public Health,* November 1990 (US). American surveillance data showing 95 per cent of 79 lesbians with AIDS surveyed had shared needles

Cole, Rebecca & Cooper, Sally, 'Lesbian Exclusion From HIV/AIDS Education: Ten years of low-risk identity and high-risk behavior', in *SIECUS Report,* December 1990 (US)

D.A.W.N., *HIV and AIDS: Facts for women who use drugs*

Denenberg, Risa, 'We Shoot Drugs, and We are Your Sisters', in *OutlLook,* Summer 1991 (US). Lesbians urged to tackle risks of HIV infection via drug use as well as sexual transmission

Einhorn, Lena, 'New Data on Lesbians and AIDS', in *off our backs,* April 1989. Report on 164 cases of AIDS among lesbians

Feminist Review No.41, 1992. Special issue on women and health with articles about women and HIV

George, Sue, 'Oral Examination', in *The Guardian*, 19 February 1992. Brief examination of lesbians and HIV transmission with information on dental dams

Heburn, Cuca & Gutierrez, Bonnie, *Alive and Well: A lesbian health guide,* Crossing Press, New York, 1988. See Chapter 5: Lesbians and AIDS

McCaskell, Lisa, 'We Are Not Immune: Women and AIDS', in *Healthsharing,* Autumn 1988. Covers safer sex for lesbians

Minkowitz, Donna, 'Safe and Sappho: An AIDS primer for lesbians', in *Village Voice,* February 1988. First US mainstream press article to discuss safer-sex issues for lesbians

Morin, Jack, *Anal Pleasure and Health: A guide for men and women,* Yes Press, California, 1989. Advice for all women, including lesbians, who engage in anal sex/play

Murray, Maria, 'Battles Joined: Odyssey of a lesbian AIDS activist', *Gay Community News,* February/March 1988 (US). Five-part series by a lesbian AIDS activist and journalist

Murray, Maria, 'Dental Dams De-Bunked', in *Sexual Health Report,* Spring 1988, Vol. 9

Perry, S. et al, 'Orogenital Transmission of HIV' (letter), in *Annals of Internal Medicine,* Vol.111:11, 1989

O'Sullivan, Sue & Thompson, Kate (eds), *Positively Women: Living with AIDS,* Sheba Feminist Publishers, London, 1992. Personal testimony plus short chapters on housing, current allopathic treatments, holistic health practices, HIV and pregnancy, drugs, safer sex and healthy living. 'Thinking About the Issue' by Hope Massiah explores ideas behind safer sex for lesbians

Panos Dosier, *Triple Jeopardy: Women and AIDS* . Panos is one of the world's leading authorities on the extent and social implications of the HIV/AIDS epidemic

Patton, Cindy, *Sex and Germs: The politics of AIDS,* South End Press, Boston,1985. An early, ardent telling of gay/lesbian grass roots political response to AIDS

Patton, Cindy, *Inventing AIDS,* Routledge, London,1990

Patton, Cindy & Kelly, Janis, *Making It: A woman's guide to sex in the age of AIDS,* Crossing Press, New York, 1987. For lesbians and straight women in Spanish and English

Patton, Cindy, 'Safe Sex and Lesbians', in *The Pink Paper,* 25 February 1988

Patton, Cindy, interview with Sue O'Sullivan in 'Perverse Politics', *Feminist Review,* No.34, 1990

Power, Lisa, 'Is HIV a Lesbian Issue?', in *The Pink Paper,* 30 August 1992

Reider, Ines & Rupplet, Patricia (eds), *Matters of Life and Death (Women Speak about AIDS)* , Virago, London, 1989. American collection of essays by lesbians facing AIDS as activists, educators and carers

Ribble, Denise, 'Not Just Another Article on Lesbian Safe Sex', in *Sappho's Isle,* July 1989. Includes a risk-assessment survey

Richardson, Diane, *Safer Sex: The guide for women today,* Pandora, London, 1990

Richardson, Diane, *Women and the AIDS Crisis,* Pandora, London, 1987

Rudd, Andrea & Taylor, Darien, *Positive Women: Voices of women Living with AIDS,* Second Story Press, Toronto, 1992. International anthology by HIV-positive women

Sabatini, M. et al, 'Kaposi's Sarcoma and T-Cell Lymphoma in an Immunodeficient Woman: A case report', in *AIDS Research,* Vol. 1, 1984

Sheba Collective, *Serious Pleasure*, Sheba Feminist Publishers, London, 1989. Section on safer sex for lesbians

Smyth, Cherry & Burston, Paul, 'Safe Sex Special', in *City Limits,* Issue 518, 5-12 September 1991. Includes exploration of safer-sex issues for lesbians

Solomon, Nancy, 'Risky Business: Should lesbians practise safer sex?', in *Out/Look,* Spring 1992

Spitzer, P.G. & Weiner N.J., 'Transmission of HIV from a Woman to a Man by Oral Sex', in *New England Journal of Medicine,* Vol. 320:251, 1989

Terrence Higgins Trust, *Benefits for People with HIV and AIDS: A handbook for advisers, April 1992-April 1993*. Clear guide on cash benefits written for advisers and social workers

White, Evelyn, *The Black Women's Health Book: Speaking for ourselves,* Seal Press, Seattle 1990. Includes voices of women from different eras, classes and sexual backgrounds

Winnow, Jackie, 'Lesbians Working On AIDS: Assessing the impact on health care for women', in *Out/Look,* Summer 1989

Winnow, Jackie, 'Lesbians Evolving Health Care: Cancer and AIDS', in *Feminist Review,* No.41, Summer 1992

Regular publications

AIDS Action: The international newsletter on AIDS prevention and control, English edition from AHRTAG, 1 London Bridge Street, London SE1 9SG. Free to readers in developing countries

AIDS Dialogue, Health Education Authority, Hamilton House, Mabledon Place, London WC1H 9TX Tel: 071 383 3833

AIDS Treatment News, PO Box 411256, San Francisco, CA 94141, US. Information on the latest treatments

Black HIV/AIDS Newsletter, 111 Devenport Road, Shepherds Bush, London W12 8PB Tel: 071 749 2828. Free

Body Positive Newsletter, 51b Philbeach Gardens, London SW5 9EB Tel: 071 835 1045. Free

HIV News Review, Information Department, Terrence Higgins Trust, 52-54 Gray's Inn Road, London WC1 8JU Tel: 071 831 0330

Mainliners Newsletter, PO Box 125, London SW9 8EF Tel: 071 737 3141. Free to HIV-positive people and drug users

National AIDS Manual, NAM Publications Ltd, Unit 52, Eurolink Business Centre, London SW2 1BZ Tel: 071 737 1846

WORLD (Women Organizing to Respond to Life-Threatening Diseases), PO Box 11535, Oakland, CA 94611, US. Newsletter for and about women facing HIV

Film and video

Clips Dir. Debbie Sundhal & Nan Kinney, 30 mins 1989 (US). Three 10-minute safer-sex porn shorts for lesbians. Available from **Out on a Limb**, 071 498 9643

Condoms are a Girl's Best Friend Dir. Eric Kay, 4 mins 1991 (US)

Current Flow Dir. Jean Carlomusto & Gregg Bordowitz, 4 mins 1989 (US). Part of the *Safer Sex Shorts* series, the tape features hot, safe lesbian sex. Available from **Out on a Limb**, 071 498 9643

Diana's Hair Ego: AIDS info up front, Dir. Ellen Spiro, 29 mins 1990 (US)

Doctors, Liars, Women Dir. Jean Carlomusto & Maria Maggenti, 23 mins 1988 (US). Portrait of ACT UP New York's lesbian caucus in action against the publication of a misleading *Cosmopolitan* article about HIV transmission and unprotected heterosexual sex

Falling through the Cracks Dir. Amber Hollibaugh, 10 mins 1991 (US). Margie Riverra shares her experience as a woman with AIDS

Her Giveaway Dir. Renee White Rabbit, 20 mins 1988 (US)

Latex and Lace Dir. Sutton Laird et al, 22 mins 1988 (US). Lesbians, bisexual and straight women talk about AIDS

No Glove, No Love Dir. Inka Petersen & Anja Schultz, 1 min 1991 (Germany)

Report from the Amsterdam AIDS Conference Dir. Penny Ashbrook in the *OUT* news bulletin, transmitted 5 August 1992, Channel 4 (UK)

Party Safe Dir. Ellen Spiro, 24 mins 1992 (US). Mixed safer-sex party

Prowling by Night Dir. Gwendolyn, 5 mins 1990 (Canada). Animated, promoting safer sex on the streets

Reframing AIDS Dir. Pratibha Parmar, 38 mins 1988 (UK)

Safer Play Dir. Shakila Maan (for the Naz HIV Project), 3 mins 1992 (UK)

Safer Sex Shorts 25 mins 1990 (US). Annie Sprinkle demonstrates safer sex for lesbians in one of the five shorts

Skin Dir. Colin Campbell, 18 mins 1990 (Canada)

The Sluts and Goddesses Video, or How to be a Sex Goddess in 101 Easy Steps Dir. Maria Beatty & Annie Sprinkle, 50 mins 1992 (US)

Suburban Dykes Stars Sharon Mitchell from *Kamakaze Hearts,* Fatale Video/Blush Entertainment (US). Available through **Out on a Limb**, 071 498 9643

Target City Hall Dir. DIVA TV, 28 mins 1989 (US). Documents the massive demonstration by ACT UP New York at City Hall, March 1989

Testing the Limits Guide to Safer Sex Dir. TTL Collective, 28 mins 1990 (US). Engaging and humorous instruction of safer sex with Nurse Ribble

Voices from the Front Dir. Sandra Elgear, Robyn Hunt, David Meiera, 50 mins 1990 (US)

Out from Scarlet Press

Lesbians Talk Queer Notions

Cherry Smyth

The 1990s has produced a new political radicalism within the lesbian and gay communities, with the emergence of activist groups such as OutRage, ACT UP and Queer Nation, with their 'we're here, we're queer, get used to it' agendas. But what is this queer politics? Does the new defiance signal a meaningful shift in ideology, or is it merely the wishful thinking of a few white gay men? Are queer politics and feminism in any way compatible? What does queer mean for lesbians, and who is setting the agenda? Is queer a positive alliance or a watering down of lesbian strength? Is there a queer aesthetic? Cherry Smyth describes the development of the new politics and discusses its implications with an international group of activists and their critics.

ISBN 1 85727 025 8

Lesbians Talk Issues

Lesbian politics in the 1990s is producing a fast-changing agenda of issues and debates, contradictions and differences of opinion. The **Lesbians Talk Issues** series is designed to provide a forum in which topics of current interest within the international lesbian community can be dissected and discussed with immediacy and flexibility.

If you would like to write a pamphlet in response to any of the issues raised in ***Lesbians Talk (Safer) Sex*** *or on any other topical area of lesbian debate, please write to Scarlet Press, 5 Montague Road, London E8 2HN*